SLICES OF LIFE

*A collection of traditional Irish short stories, radio talks,
feature articles and romance fiction from the published
works of Tony Brehony*

BOOKS BY THE SAME AUTHOR

West Cork- "a sort of a history like..."

"Visitors to West Cork will find it both enlightening and entertaining for it is a fund of local history. Every household should have a copy.
Damien Enright. *Irish Examiner.*

Theirs not to do or die..

There are not many books set in World War Two that will make you laugh but this is a definite exception. Brehony writes in the bawdy robust Navy language of that era which makes you feel like you too are ocean-bound with his rather dubious bunch of heroes. A fun read.
Moira Hannon. *The Star.*

SLICES OF LIFE

A collection of traditional Irish short stories, radio talks, feature articles and romance fiction from the published works of Tony Brehony

TONY BREHONY

First Published by AB BOOKS
7 ST BRIGID'S DRIVE
CLONDALKIN
DUBLIN 22

Printed by RYLE PRINT GROUP

ISBN: 0-9541410-1-6

Dedicated to my grandchildren:

Mark, Daragh, Eve, Neil, Jodie, Ruth, Clara, Sarah and Aaron

TABLE OF CONTENTS

AS IT WAS IN THE BEGINNING

RTÉ, *Sunday Miscellany*, October 2003

In the autumn of 1952, *The Cork Examiner* advertised that its Christmas edition, *The Hollybough*, would carry short stories by "Ireland's leading writers, Tony Brehony and John B. Keane."

I had never heard of John B. Keane and I'm sure he had never heard of me but by happy chance, a year or so later, we met in a pub in Doneraile, the village in Cork, where John was working. Over a few pints, it didn't take long to establish that we had much in common apart from our literary aspirations. We were both engaged to be married and we both accepted the fact that, at our level of income, there was absolutely no way we could ever afford to get married. John was earning two pounds ten shillings a week as an assistant in the local chemist's shop and I had just been demobbed from the Royal Navy with a war pension, which barely topped £3 a week. And despite *The Cork Examiner's* euphemistic suggestion that we were Ireland's leading writers, our literary earnings weren't impressive either – and worse, John's first novel had just been rejected and I was suffering from early writer's block.

That's when I told him that I was sick and tired of the poverty-level wages which writing short stories was bringing in and I was going to make a fresh start – I had secured a real job with a company in Dublin paying £12 a week with a car supplied, and my writing career would have to go on a very long finger.

"Twelve quid a week and a motorcar!" John B.'s eyes were alight with his envy. "Jaysus, boy, if I could get something like that I'd be outa this kip in the morning."

So after much more liquid deliberation on the vicissitudes of life and literature, I promised John with boozy confidence that I'd get him a job in the same company in Dublin – I had, I assured him, the right connections. He agreed eagerly to hold himself on a 24-hour stand-by for my call and he gave me addresses in both Doneraile and Listowel where I could contact him urgently by telegram. We celebrated our new positive approach to life with a few more pints and then we went our separate ways.

I never met John B. Keane again but for the next 30 years I watched his climb to the top of the literary ladder. Over the same 30 years I struggled up my own rickety ladder in the murky world of industry and, until I retired, never once put a creative pen to paper.

Looking back now at my meagre contribution to Irish literature since those heady days long ago when *The Cork Examiner* nominated me and John B. Keane as Ireland's leading writers, I can only plead that, unlike John, I peaked too early. On the positive side, however, there is the fact that my failure to get John B. Keane a real job in 1952 ensured that the world of literature was privileged to savour his genius to the full. For that surely I deserve some acclaim. We who are not giants must content ourselves with lesser things.

THE DAY I DANCED
WITH EVITA PERON

RTÉ, *Sunday Miscellany*, September 1977

For a few brief minutes back in the late '40s, my path crossed that of the beautiful Eva Peron of Argentina. I held her in my arms and we danced a slow foxtrot, if not cheek-to-cheek, then as close as any man may dance with another man's wife, especially when that man is looking on in tolerant amusement, but even more so when he happens to be the President and Dictator of the country you are visiting. Juan Peron was reputed to have blood on his hands and I didn't particularly want any of it to be mine.

There are not too many men left in the world today who danced with Eva of Argentina – who knows, I may even be the last! It is as a member of that endangered species that I wish to place the facts on record.

It was in the late '40s and I was a young officer in the Royal Navy. We were working out of Bermuda and engaged on a post-war propaganda mission of flag-waving in South America. Twelve hours out of Buenos Aires we hove-to in mid ocean, every man jack was ordered over the side and that ship was painted from mast-head to water-line in a matter of hours. Then, fresh as our new paint, gleaming grey and with all the brass-work shining, we moved majestically up into the mouth of the River Plate and past the point where the German battleship, *Graf Spee* had been battered into cruel self-destruction a few years before.

Buenos Aires welcomed us with open arms. The official visits and counter visits started as soon as we tied up to the wall, and we were informed that General Peron and his wife, Eva, would make an official visit to the ship the next day.

Again there was the usual flurry of scrubbing and polishing of brass. The official party arrived, the guard of honour was inspected, the Marine band played the national anthem and we retired to the wardroom for drinks. My moment of entry into the long history of Argentina was at hand.

General Peron, a formidable figure standing over six feet tall and resplendent in army uniform chatted amiably with the Admiral. Eva Peron, slim, blonde and strikingly beautiful in a tight-fitting black frock, was at her best, surrounded as she was by 16 attentive naval officers. The interpreter could hardly keep up with her effervescent chatter as she turned on a radiant charm that had us all bewitched, and flitted from one to the other like a colourful butterfly.

She was opposite me when the Marine band, now on the quarterdeck, broke into a slow foxtrot. The change of tempo from the previous martial airs was almost startling. Eva broke off in mid sentence, her brown eyes sparkling in a mocking smile, she reached out invitingly to me. I didn't need any interpreter to tell me what she had in mind – we melted into one another's arms and we danced.

A sudden hush had fallen on the wardroom. Over Eva's blonde head, her hair brushing my cheek, I saw her husband smiling indulgently. Her slim body touched against mine, my pulse quickened; the fragrance of her nearness was tantalising. And then, as suddenly as she had started, she broke off, squeezed my hand and stood back.

"Thank you, Senora," I whispered and bowed low. The wardroom broke into polite applause. I would like to pretend that Eva blushed but she didn't. She just turned her charm to the next officer in line and I was forgotten.

All that was over 50 years ago. Eva Peron died of cancer two years later at the age of thirty-three. She has been called many things. Her enemies called her the 'Blonde Whore'. She called herself the 'Defender of the Shirtless Ones'. Those shirtless ones, the poor of Argentina, called her 'Saint Eva'. Her body was placed in a vault in Buenos Aires, 15 feet below ground level with walls made of steel. The locks were of made of the latest burglar-proof design and an alarm system connected the vault with police headquarters.

Born in poverty, Eva became the richest and most powerful woman in the world. Her detractors claim that she was at the centre of every racket in Argentina. She was, they say, a vicious enemy, a scheming witch, and a woman with blood on her hands. One writer said of her: "There was a fatal fascination about Eva Peron that remains even after her death – an aura of evil that has become a legend."

Be that as it may, for my own part, I have but one fact to present before the bar of history – Eva Peron was not a very good ballroom dancer. In fact, like we used to say down the country, as far as the slow foxtrot was concerned, Eva had two left feet. May she rest forever in peace.

THE WOMAN WHO WATCHED

Radio Eireann, October 1951

The first thing I noticed about Martha O'Brien was the quavering venom in her voice. "So! You're the new doctor, eh? Dr Daly, isn't it?"

I nodded, rather at a loss as she studied me coldly, her rheumy eyes taking in everything, missing nothing. She was propped up in a massive four-poster bed, a lace shawl thrown loosely around her shoulders, a cup of tea in her hand.

"And as useless as your predecessors, no doubt." She sipped the tea, the delicate china of the cup seeming to merge into her yellowing skin as if it were an extension of the talon-like hand. I smiled, embarrassed, and all the time her eyes bored through me.

I had taken over the small practice in this remote west of Ireland village only a week before and though my housekeeper had warned me about the "rather strange" O'Brien sisters I hadn't expected quite such a hostile reception. She sighed and put the cup of tea on the bedside table.

"Oh well, I suppose I'll have to put up with you just as I had to put up with the others. McCarthy came here five years ago – an alcoholic quack if ever there was one – and that other fellow, O'Reilly, he attended me for 30 years. I watched them come and I heard the church bell tolling when they were taken away." She permitted herself a tight-lipped smile as she pulled the shawl more closely around her shoulders.

"No doubt I'll hear the bell tolling for you too if you can stick around this village long enough. Until then, however, I want you to visit me here every Saturday morning at eleven o'clock. Is that understood?" I nodded. "Oh, there's nothing you can do for me – I've been in this bed for 50 years and I'll stay here until I die, but I'll pay your exorbitant fees just to have you visit me once a week to make sure that nothing – nothing unusual happens to me. Every week, you understand?"

She paused then and let her eyes wander to the door where her sister, Emily, stood twittering like a nervous sparrow.

"Your duties are simple – I want you to make sure that my sister Emily doesn't do away with me – poison me or such like." The utter contempt in her voice made me shudder. "My dear sister Emily hates me . . . "

I heard Emily's gasped intake of breath and then the door shut and she was gone. Martha laughed dryly and turned to me again.

"Yes, my dear sister hates me, and she has good reasons for wanting me out of the way – not the least of them her disgusting craving for gin. You got the smell, no doubt?"

I had, but I mumbled something about not having noticed and that it was probably imagination on her part. She shushed me impatiently.

"That will be all then. Just don't forget – every Saturday at eleven o'clock!" And I was dismissed with a curt wave of her bony claw.

I went down the stairs glad to be out of that bedroom, but before I could let myself out the front door I heard a whispered call.

"Dr Daly – I wonder if I could have a word with you

for a minute – about my sister . . . "

Emily was standing at the drawing-room door, a glass half full of gin in her hand. Her eyes were sparkling strangely and wisps of grey hair fell loosely from the bun secured at the nape of her neck. I followed her into the drawing room and she sat nervously on the edge of a chair, sipping from the glass, her eyes studying me over the rim.

"I suppose she told you that I drink?" I nodded, wondering why this rather pathetic creature had endured all those years of tending the invalid upstairs. "You're wondering why I didn't leave her years ago, aren't you?" It was uncanny the way she had read my thoughts.

"I'll tell you why, doctor – I'll tell you why I continue to live here with her, why I hate her. Oh yes, she's right, she's always right – I do hate her. The day she dies will be the happiest day of my life. I'll sing and I'll dance and I'll nail that bedroom door shut. You hear? I'll nail it shut so that nobody will ever have to go in there again while this horrible house stands . . . "

She gulped down some more gin. "Now, please, Miss O'Brien . . . " I started but she shushed me up.

"No, doctor, don't interrupt me! And don't pity me! I don't want pity, though God knows I deserve some." Her voice sank to a whisper. She stared out through the dirty windows as if she were alone in the room.

"Father loved her. He loved her so much that there was no room for even a little affection for me. When she was paralysed after a riding accident he looked after her, hand and foot, right up to the day he died. He left everything to her, every penny and every stick of furniture. And he trapped me forever by putting a clause in the will leaving everything to me on her death providing that I stayed here to care for her. Before I realised what a hell he had trapped me in, I was too old to leave, too old to start out with nothing. That's why she's so afraid that I'll kill her. That's why she tortures me by living on and on. I wait on her hand and foot. Every night at nine o'clock I have to read to her from *Wuthering Heights* – read and read till she falls asleep. *Wuthering Heights* – always *Wuthering Heights*." She turned to me. "Have you ever read *Wuthering Heights*, doctor?" I shook my head.

"No-o, I'm afraid I never got around to it – never had much time for casual reading, you know . . . " She nodded but she didn't hear me.

"*Wuthering Heights* – I know every word of that book by heart. Every night, night after night for 50 years I've read it to her. As soon as I finish the last page I have to start all over again – always the same book – never a change – always *Wuthering Heights*. Oh God, how I hate that book. I hate it almost as much as I hate her . . . " A bell clanged dismally through the empty stillness of the house. Emily snapped out of her reverie, her burning eyes turning up to the ceiling and then back to me.

"Never a moment's peace – always something." She threw back the remains of the glass of gin and came over to me. She smiled a slow pathetic smile and for a moment she almost looked beautiful.

"I'm sorry I can't entertain you any longer, doctor, but I must go to her now." She looked me straight in the eyes and then she signed. "Don't worry, doctor, I've no intention of doing away with her. I'd love to – more than anything else in the world, but I just don't have the courage." And she left me and headed off towards the kitchen. Poor, poor woman, I thought, and then I left, glad to get away from the clinging depression in the house.

Martha died two days later. I remember how surprised I was when I got the message – surprised and worried.

An awful doubt nagged away inside me as I drove up to the house. Had Emily been finally driven to take the steps that Martha feared?

Emily met me at the door. I was shocked at the change in her. Gone was the air of frightened self-pitying depression. Her eyes sparkled with new life and she welcomed me with a chirpy laugh. Her breath smelt heavily of gin.

"Oh, do come in, doctor – come on in! I'm so glad to see you again, and so soon. Isn't it wonderful? You must join me in a celebratory drink – a toast to my dear sister who has gone from us . . ."

She laughed again when she saw the shock on my face. I pushed past her rather curtly and hurried upstairs. She followed me, a constant flow of chatter on her lips.

"You mustn't think I had anything to do with her death, doctor – she just died. When I came up this morning, there she was – dead! I could scarcely believe it – oh, dear me, what a pleasant surprise it was. Good morning, Martha, I said but there wasn't a sound from her – not even her usual bad-tempered grunt. Dead – absolutely dead! Oh, doctor, are you terribly shocked at my attitude? But you know how we felt about each other, my dear sister and I."

She sat on the edge of a chair and watched me in silence while I examined the body. With a sigh of relief I realised that Emily was right – Martha had apparently died a natural death. Emily saw the relief on my face.

"There, there, my dear doctor, how could you distrust me so? I told you! But let's get out of this awful room and have a little drink, shall we?" She looked for a moment at the grim cold face of her sister.

"Tomorrow, when she's gone, I'll close this room – close it for ever – I'll nail it shut." She pointed at a toolbox beside the door. "I've got the hammer and nails all ready – see? And nobody will ever have to come in here again."

She went to the bedside table and picked up a heavy leather-bound book. "*Wuthering Heights,*" she whispered, looking down at the corpse. "I'll never, never have to read a line of it to you again." With a quick almost contemptuous gesture she handed me the book. "You never read this classic, you told me." Her lips twitched in a quick smile. "Take it, doctor – read it – burn it – do whatever you like with it, but take it out of my sight. I never want to see this horrible book again . . . " And she ran out of the room, tears streaming down her face.

It was four days after the funeral when I saw Emily again. I had been out on a late call and it was two in the morning when I got home. Wearily I checked the pad by the telephone – there was just one message left by my housekeeper. I read it again and again in disbelief. "Miss Emily O'Brien called for the book that she lent you."

What in the world had come over Emily that she wanted that book back? But I was much too tired to worry about her eccentric behaviour at that hour of the morning and I went up to my room. I looked out the window up into the darkness of the night towards the big house on the hill and suddenly I knew that something was wrong – very wrong.

Beckoning from the top of the hill was a single light, like some malevolent unblinking eye. I looked at my watch again – 2.30. Could Emily be ill? Why else would she be up at this hour of the morning? I sighed and went back down stairs and got out the car. I wouldn't be able to sleep anyway – that light would be worrying me all night.

I was glad I had a torch with me. When I reached the front door I lifted the heavy knocker but before I could bang it down, the door creaked open under the weight of my hand. I felt a cold inexplicable shiver ripple through me. I flashed the torch around the hall and complete darkness swallowed up the cutting beam. The house was filled with silence – awful silence.

I found the hall light and switched it on. I called out again but there was no reply. Slowly I ascended the carpeted stairs. I saw a chink of light coming from under a door – Martha's room! I hurried along the corridor, calling out to Emily but still there was no response. My pounding heart was beating a muffled tattoo that seemed to ring through the house.

I stopped in amazement at Martha's door, it had been nailed shut, just as Emily had told me it would be, but the nails had been extracted. I turned the knob slowly and gave the door a gentle push. It creaked open. I stood there in frozen horror and took in the scene before me, sweat beading my brow.

The room was cold – cold and evil, the light from the bedside lamp casting long eerie shadows. The massive four-poster dominated everything. Martha's lace shawl was thrown loosely on the pillows. The armchair was drawn up beside the bed. And Emily, poor Emily, her body was stiffly upright in the chair, her head lolling back, her dead face twisted in awful agonised horror. And open on her lap, ready to read, read, read, even into eternity, was the leather-bound volume of *Wuthering Heights*.

WRITE YOUR NAME
INTO HISTORY

RTÉ, *Sunday Miscellany*, June 1981

This coming Summer when you're writing your postcards
lazing on the beach in Rosscarbery or Baltimore or where-
ever, don't just make banal statements like "Wish you
were here" or "The weather is great and the craic is 90!"
– you may be missing out on a glorious opportunity to
write your name into Irish history in a few hundred years'
time.

Way back in 1689, an officer of King James, one Captain
John Stevens, no doubt sitting bored out of his head on
the beach in Bantry, wrote to a friend in England:

*"Bantry is a miserable poor place, not
worthy of the name of a town, having not
above 7 or 8 little houses, the rest being
very mean cottages."*

Today, nearly five hundred years on, his name and his
opinion of Bantry is still quoted by historians. Now, if he
had contented himself by recording the fact that it was
raining as usual that morning in Bantry, his observation
would have passed into the realms of the forgotten, and
the world would never have heard of Captain John Stevens.

Again, a few years later, in 1691, a Rev. Richard Allyn
writing from Kinsale had this to say:

*"The town of Kinsale is a large stinking
filthy hole that has nothing good in it. I
will be glad to leave so vile a place..."*

And today, because his pithy opinions of Kinsale are constantly quoted, the name of the Rev. Richard Allyn lives on. It would appear that because he said the wrong thing at the right time – or the right thing at the wrong time – his name will be remembered as long as historians research and write the history of Kinsale.

Now, just to make sure you understand: though the back door into the pages of historic fame and immortality is standing wide open to welcome you, there are still ways you could mess up your entry.

In 1914, a simple sailor whose ship was visiting Bantry, wrote a postcard to his sweetheart, Lily. He said: *"Bantry is a dirty little hole full of pubs, pigs and fowls - they all seem to live together."*

Again, notice, no inane remarks about the weather nor soulful wishes that his darling Lily could be there with him. No, just a colourful description of Bantry as he saw it. And 80 years later, his postcard has become a research item for historians. Unfortunately, however, he didn't sign his name so he missed his opportunity to pass through the gates of history. However, the postcard has ensured that his sweetheart, Lily Tapley, 18 Albert Terrace, Old Road, Plymouth, has taken her rightful place in the annals of Bantry town.

So remember – this summer, when you write those postcards to your loved ones at home, think hard, look around you, and record those things about your holiday resort that the travel agent never mentions. And sign your name clearly as you place the facts on record. Who knows? In a few hundred years' time some historian, sifting fact from fiction, may fasten on the information recorded in your postcard. Then, like Captain Stevens and the Rev. Richard Allyn, your name too could be indelibly inscribed on the eternal pages of history.

THE LONG NIGHT OF
ALL THE SOULS

Cork Hollybough, December 1950

It couldn't be snow – not on All Souls' Night, not that early in the year! Another light flurry of big wet flakes, flying and flashing in the darkening moonlight, sent panic flooding through Martin's weary body. Snow, snow, snow – just like that other All Souls' Night, 46 long years ago, the night the Fusiliers took the village in Belgium, the night the German army retreated, the night of the snow. Would the haunting memory never leave him?

But it hadn't been snow that night – it was only bread, little roundy bits of bread!

"Only bits of fecking bread!" Martin shouted defiantly lashing out at the flying flakes swirling about his shoulders, and the echo of his voice came back to him on the chill, mocking wind: "Bread? Only bread?"

Martin clinched his eyes trying to shut out the clawing memory of that ruined chapel, the smashed tabernacle, the scattered chalices.

"Bread! Bloody bleedin' bread and feck-all else," he whispered fiercely, afraid now to shout, afraid of the doubting echoes that returned to haunt him down the years.

His numbed hands clutched the battered violin case hugging it to his chest. For 40 years now he had tramped the lonely roads of Ireland, fiddling a few tunes in the pubs, begging a few drinks, always alone and forever searching for the peace of mind that never came, and always haunted by those swirling flakes of... of bread.

And now it was the Feast of All Souls again – he could sense their presence around him, the friends who had died by his side and the Jerries he had killed. But the long weary years had not dulled the memory of the night in Belgium, the night of the looting... the night of the snow.

He squared his shoulders defiantly and hunched into the wind. There would be warmth and drink and blessed forgetfulness in the town ahead. The fiddle would charm the melancholy thoughts away and the whiskey would ward off the spirits of the friends who had died in the bloody battle to take the little chapel.

It was Jock who said it about the snow when he emptied the contents of the chalice over Martin's head. "Here y'are, Paddy – snow!" And the white flakes had tumbled around his shoulders. But it wasn't snow – it was bread, little white roundy bits of bread. Three days afterwards they got rid of the stolen chalices.

Martin shuddered, but it wasn't the cold. They were well behind the lines then and Jock found a Frenchman who was willing to take the stuff off their hands, and no questions asked. And the price had been good. He could still remember the cold calculating eyes striking a mean between the value of the stuff melted down and the value of the money to the two Tommies in need of francs for more satisfying soul-quenching cognac. Then they found themselves a bistro and the drinking started – drinking, drinking to kill the terrible memory and the nagging conscience. And year after year it went on – All Souls' Night to All Souls' Night – always scrubbing at the conscience with whiskey, always trying to clean the slate, and never, never succeeding.

A light flickering through the trees brought Martin's weariness surging up to engulf him. He was no longer the light-hearted Fusilier who had marched from the Normandy beachhead right up into Germany, laughing at the danger and the tiredness. His days were numbered now and when death came he would open his arms in welcome relief.

No point, he decided, in passing a friendly light and wandering on into the lonely darkness searching for a town that might have a friendly pub. He rattled the violin-case gently. There was nearly half a bottle of poitín in there and that would see him through the night. Where there was a light there might be a little heat and comfort, even if only in a barn with some hay to warm his chilled old body. This All Souls' Night was just another night – only his mind made it different, his mind and the memory of the swirling snow about his shoulders.

The building was small and old but anywhere would do to kip – all he needed was a roof over his head. His hopeful push made the door creak open. He peered in curiously and his heart gave a sickening lurch. He looked fearfully around, his tired mind slowly taking in the situation. It was a chapel – a small chapel, just like the last chapel he'd been in over 40 years ago in Belgium; the night of the snow. Here y'are, Paddy – snow! But it hadn't been snow . . .

Martin backed out in panic, his watery eyes blinding him. A priest was saying Mass. He'd heard talk of this new-fangled thing – evening Mass. There was no evening Mass in his day. Come to think about it, he couldn't even remember the last time he was at Mass. He pulled himself together, a little of the old bravado spirit warming through his veins. Why should he be afraid? This was shelter – just the same as a barn or a pub.

He took the bottle of poitín out of his violin case and took a long hard shuddering swallow. Then he shuffled quietly into the back seat and flopped down onto his knees. He smiled grimly as he scraped back onto the seat – after all those years, old habits die hard. His eyes closed to the scene in front of him, ignoring the congregation that filled the chapel. He had found shelter and peace at last – except for the nagging voice of the shagging priest on the altar. A bell tinkled musically and impinged on his blankness.

"Take this, all of you, and eat it; this is My Body which will be given up for you . . . "

Martin's eyes opened in panic. The priest's hands were raised high above his head and the little white disc seemed to flood Martin's whole vision. The disc, as white as snow . . .

"Here y'are, Paddy, snow!"

"This is My Body!"

No, no, that was bread – it was Jock who said it was snow!

Martin froze in horror. Just three seats ahead of him, Jock turned around and smiled back at him as if he, too, was remembering that night. And sweet Jasus, there was Tommy and Packy and – and Chalkey White sitting with him. But how could that be? He was on the detail that buried the four of them in a shallow grave beside the road that day they strayed into a minefield outside Oldenburgh.

And, sweet God, there were Jerry soldiers in the congregation too – he could tell by the markings on their uniforms, they were the crowd that occupied the little chapel in Belgium the night the Fusiliers attacked. Oh my God, he groaned, realisation slowly dawning on him – 'tis the Long Night of All the Souls – they're all back . . .

Martin stumbled in his panic to get out, to escape from this new horror from his past. The door slammed behind him and he found himself in the darkness of what he realised was the confession box. No matter. It shut THEM out. There was peace in here – no ghosts from his past, no chanting, no snow to haunt him.

His breath came in sobbing gasps, a stabbing pain tightening in his chest. He fumbled for the violin case to get the bottle out. He didn't hear the scraping sound when the slide of the confessional was opened.

Martin jerked in fright and he felt the hair rise coldly on the back of his neck – the bearded face of a young priest behind the grill smiled at him. Oh, God, no it couldn't be him – not after all those years. He and Jock had pushed the battered body out of their way when they went into the chapel, when they went up on the altar. He'd never forget that face, the blood oozing from the corner of the bearded mouth, the battered head . . .

"Oh my God!" The strangled groan died in Martin's throat, panic swelling the pain in his heaving chest.

"Tell it!" The whispered words were strangely compelling. "Confess and be forgiven."

The words came babbling out of Martin's mouth, hesitant at first and then like a gushing torrent.

"In Belgium, Father, that night long ago – this night it was, All Souls' Night – Jock and meself, we went into the chapel – 'twas all bombed and wrecked and you tried to stop us – I mean a priest tried to stop us and I belted you – him – over the head with the butt of my rifle and then Jock prised the door off the tabernacle and we stole the chalices. "Here y'are, Paddy, snow!" Jock said and he emptied a chalice over me head and then we made off and we sold the lot to this French fella and we drank and we drank and we drank . . . "

Martin's voice babbled on, the words tumbling and falling from his lips like snow melting in the sun and running away, washing and cleaning and healing and leaving him weak in unbelieving happiness when he heard the blessed words of forgiveness whispering through the box. It hadn't been snow like Jock said, and it hadn't been bread either, he knew that now.

Martin's weary body slumped to the cold floor. A shaft of pale moonlight beamed down through the roofless chapel and lit up what was left of the ruined walls held together by centuries of creeping, clinging ivy. It settled like a protecting shroud around Martin's body. He was still clutching the battered violin case to his chest. He was home at last. The long, weary march was over.

DROWNING THE SHAMROCK

Irish Independent, September 1989

In the port of Trincomalee, on the east coast of what was then Ceylon, Saint Patrick's Day 1942 was no different to any other dreary day in that dilapidated and un-distinguished outpost of Britain's far-flung Empire. The oppressive heat, the endless clip-clop of horse-drawn gharries, the aimless groups of bored, white-clad sailors, they all added urgency to Trincomalee's frantic efforts to reap some financial benefit from this unexpected bonanza – the British Eastern Fleet was in port.

Walking through the blacked-out streets I wondered why I had bothered to come ashore – there was nothing to see, nothing to do and nowhere to go. And then I heard it – a soft, sad voice lifted in song, barely audible above the whining babble of the cajoling beggars who were everywhere. At first I could hardly believe what I was hearing – the words in Irish brought me straight back to my old schoolroom in West Cork where, just a couple of years before, I had first heard them:

"Mise Eamonn a' Cnuic ata baite, fuar fliuch o shior suil sleite 'gus gleannta . . . "

It took but a minute to locate the cafe where the singing sailor sat alone at a corner table, a bottle of beer in front of him. His only audience was the grinning Ceylonese waiter beating out an accompanying tattoo with the palms of his hands on the wooden bar counter. I waited appreciatively till the song ended.

"Bail o Dhia ar an obair," I applauded. The sailor almost jumped in surprise and then drained the bottle of beer in a long satisfying gulp. *"An bhail cheadna ort,"* he said back to me, *"agus go mairid na mna go deo!"*

And for the next five hours we drowned the shamrock as only two lonely Irishmen far from home could drown it. My new companion – Sean is all I can remember of his name – was from Ring, County Waterford and his natural fluency brought my own rusty Irish tripping back happily to my tongue. Not a word of English was spoken for the rest of the night. We sang Irish songs, we recalled long-forgotten Irish poems and as we drank the warm local-brewed beer we sighed nostalgically for those long, cool pints of good Irish Guinness that were so, so very far away. But despite the stink and the heat and the harassing flies our thoughts and our hearts were with our loved ones back in Ireland. And England's wars were a million miles away.

We parted at midnight, Sean to return to the cruiser, *Cornwall* and I to the aircraft carrier, *Indomitable*. We never met again. Just a few weeks later, on Easter Sunday, *Cornwall* was attacked by Japanese forces and sank with all hands into the vast loneliness of the Bay of Bengal.

In August the mail from home caught up with us. For me there was a small green box with a picture of a very severe-looking Saint Patrick driving the snakes out of Ireland. The shamrock inside was withered and limp and dry. God rest my poor mother, every year right through the war, a similar box arrived, anything from a month to six months after Saint Patrick's Day. But it always arrived and it always reminded me of who I was and where I had come from.

And looking back now over 60 years I can't help

thinking what a pity it was that Sean and I hadn't a sprig of my mother's shamrock to wear that Saint Patrick's night in far-off Trincomalee. Withered or not, it would have made our day.

CHRISTMAS DAY ON ADDU ATOLL

RTÉ, *Sunday Miscellany*, December 2002

It was Christmas Day 1941 and a world at war had forgotten the message of Christmas – Peace on Earth to all Mankind! The exception, perhaps, was the tiny Maldive island of Addu Atoll, 20 or so miles south of the equator and 300 miles southwest of Sri Lanka. There in a vast deep-water lagoon, a supply ship and an escorting Royal Navy frigate lay at anchor waiting to rendezvous with an aircraft carrier hastily despatched from England to provide badly needed aircover for the depleted Far East Fleet. As we waited, we prepared to celebrate Christmas on Addu Atoll.

Addu Atoll is the southern-most island of the Maldives, a group of more than two thousand coral islands, mostly uninhabited, which dot the vast blue of the Indian Ocean. The sun blazed out of a cloudless sky. Calm glass-like seas broke into long white wavelets lapping the shimmering beach. Tall palm trees formed the only horizon. The nearest people were hundreds of miles away. To us, after long weeks at sea, this was paradise.

I was one of a group of ten crewmen lucky enough to be allowed go ashore in the afternoon watch on Christmas Day. The whaler was lowered and our provisions, including a football and cricket gear, were loaded. "Have a Merry Christmas," called the quartermaster.

"And a Merry Christmas to you too," we called back

happily, our rum ration still warming inside us. And manning the oars, we pulled with a will for the welcoming shore.

Now, I was but 18 months out of Ireland, a true Celt with skin so fair that even West Cork's watery sunshine had, on occasions, turned it a nasty red. We were dressed in the official rig of the day for the tropics: a pair of shorts, a cap and a pair of sandals. I knew I was in trouble long before we reached the shore. The temperature was 90 degrees. The hot sun, blazing from an empty sky, burnt into my tender shoulders. There was no shelter, no shade and no breeze. By the time we pulled the boat out of the water and I managed to scramble over the hot sand to find the comforting shelter of a palm tree, the damage was already done – the skin of my exposed body was baked to a burning, sickening red.

The remainder of that Christmas Day is but a sorry, hazy memory. I stayed put for four miserable hours under the scanty shade of the palm tree. I nibbled at my corned-beef sandwich and I drank copiously from our supply of warm lime juice. I was never so glad in all my life when, eventually, we climbed back on board the frigate. "Enjoy your Christmas, lad?" asked the quartermaster. I passed him in discreet silence.

That was all of 60 years ago. I had forgotten Addu Atoll until last month when I saw a colourful ad in *The Sunday Times*. 'Visit the Paradise Island of the Maldives this Christmas' it invited. I read it through. Unbelievably, it was Addu Atoll they were talking about – but apparently a transformed Addu Atoll, a new exotic playground for fun-seekers, another shrine for sun-worshippers, a paradise on earth. 'Enjoy an experience never to be forgotten', the ad went on to say in lurid headlines. For a moment or two I was tempted. Why not? I thought. It could be a memorable return to an almost forgotten past. But then, suddenly, the skin on my back started to glow, as if in terrible memory. So no, I've decided that I won't be spending another Christmas on Addu Atoll – not even if they took me there for free, thank you very much!

THE LOVE MATCH

Radio Eireann, December 1953

Maybe love isn't the right word to describe the strange gnawing feeling that Percy Murphy's landlady provoked deep down in his brawny chest. No, indeed! – rather, perhaps, an affectionate interest in her wellbeing, a manly desire to protect an unfortunate widow from the clawing tentacles of a greedy masculine world, maybe even a touch of male chauvinism – but love? Well, living as they were within sight of Lisdoonvarna, the International Centre of Organised Marital Bliss, it was, perhaps, an understandable feeling.

Granted, mark you, that Percy's landlady had money – lots of it, if local gossip could be taken as true. Granted also that Percy had no money, that he was getting on in years and that his future looked pretty bleak. But let us rise above such pettiness! The woman came with the money and the money came with the woman. If you married one, you, more or less, had to take the other.

Life isn't that simple, of course – there are always snags, and there were snags in Percy's case. Actually, he had made proposals of marriage to his landlady on five different occasions; and five times she had put him off. Not refused him, no, definitely not refused! At fifty-two plus, a woman does not refuse a man – she puts him off, puts him on the long finger, so to speak. And that's where Percy was – on Matilda's long marital finger.

Matilda McArdle, the good woman in question, was a fine presentable class of a person – a widow, her husband,

God rest his soul in peace, dead long enough to be respectfully forgotten. There was a fine big house, itself and every stick of furniture in it long since paid for, and eight boarders steady the whole year round.

Why, no matter how you'd look at it, Matilda was a highly desirable woman. And in case you're the type who worries about trivialities, she wasn't difficult to look at either – a bit plump, perhaps, a little heavy here and there maybe, but must a man always seek perfection? And money? Percy thought not.

However, there came a day, a dismal day, when Percy's love campaign almost came to an abrupt end. He had proposed his usual proposal just a week before and had, as usual, been put off. Needless to say he was inclined to be a little grumpy as he sat there in his accepted place at the head of the breakfast-table chewing morosely on the bacon and the sausages.

You could almost hear his affectionate thoughts as his eyes darted around his seven fellow-lodgers. Seven eights are 56, carry five, seven fours are 28, add the five and you've got 336. Three hundred and thirty-six quid in notes paid over to Matilda every Friday night. Not bad, eh? Not bad at all! A fellow'd have to do a lot of clerking for Bord na Mona and, between PAYE, PRSI and the devil knows what else, 'twould be a long time before you'd see the colour of that sort of money – and all of it straight into her fist! Janey Mac!

Percy bit into his lip at the vexation of it. You'd think that Matilda'd only be too glad to marry a fine, honest upstanding bachelor like himself and he barely over the sixty mark. But no – she had to dilly and dally.

The object of his romantic thoughts dumped another rasher onto his plate, smiled into his eyes and returned to the kitchen. Percy grunted. And then came the words that cut into his very heart. It was Jimmy Hannigan who spoke. There was no malice aforethought in his remark, but the words were spiked and they dug into Percy's naked soul.

"I hear," said Jimmy, keeping his voice down so that it wouldn't be heard in the kitchen, "that we'll be getting ourselves a landlord after all these years. I got it down at Pat Joe's last night – Pat Joe's wife that's making the match . . . "

He paused for a melodramatic second and his eyes swivelled around his silent audience. "Guard O'Donovan it is who's getting our Matilda. 'Tis almost fixed for them to get married in the New Year . . . "

There was a silence you could hear 'twas so loud. Nobody commented, yet nobody was surprised – after all, this was matchmaking country. Wasn't Lisdoonvarna just down the road? And if any of them suspected that Percy had, on five separate occasions, thrown his hat into Matilda's ring, well, they kept their silence. They were gentlemen, these men of the bog. They chewed on their bacon and they chewed on their sausages, but they held their peace. Percy wiped his mouth with the sleeve of his coat and left the room. His heart was a miserable knot inside him but, fair dues to him, his head was high.

All through that miserable day he brooded and he smouldered. The figures in his ledger kept adding up to the same figure: 336. An unfortunate Garda who rang the office to enquire about the price of some peat briquettes was insulted and never knew why. If Matilda was going to marry a guard, and God bless the mark, Guard O'Donovan out of all of them, words failed Percy at the thought of it. But he bore his terrible pain in silence.

That evening, after a long walk across the spongy heather, so clean so sweet smelling, the bitterness inside him still bit at him and gnawed. If Matilda chose to marry a half fool when Percy's heart was cast at her feet for the taking, well . . .

"Percy! Percy, me owld friend, me fellow-lodger, how's she cuttin' . . . "

Jimmy Hannigan's ringing hail cut through Percy's dismal thoughts. Jimmy had staggered out of Daly's pub, his round good-natured face aglow with the warmth of the spirits he had already imbibed.

"Come on in and have a drink with me, Percy boy," wheedled Jimmy. "Just the wan for the road before we go home?" He lurched and a packet wrapped in brown paper splashed to the ground from under the coat he was carrying on his arm. For long staggering seconds he tried to focus on it. Then a bleary light of intoxicated understanding dawned on his face when Percy picked up the packet and a rasher fell out.

"'Tis the rashers," he said in relief, "the rashers Matilda asked me to get for the supper! So that's where they were all the time, eh? – in me coat pocket. Now who'd ha' thought that, eh? Well, well, well . . . "

Percy took Jimmy firmly by the elbow and steered him gently past the pub door. "Perhaps 'twould be better if we went home with the rashers, Jimmy," he offered.

"Matilda'll be waiting for them." Jimmy nodded foolishly, his face screwed into an effort of concentrated thought. He staggered to a stop.

"Matilda!" he shouted. "Sure, that's the very thing – knew there was something I wanted you for, Percy me pal." He pulled Percy around to face him. His voice sank to what he thought was a conspiratorial whisper.

"Look it, Percy," he said, "I was thinking about this, I was thinking why don't you marry our Matilda and save us all from that bloody Guard O'Donovan, eh?" His hard finger prodded out the punctuation marks on Percy's chest. "I was only saying to the lads this morning, Percy, after you left that if you'd marry our Matilda, then we could all still be one big happy family. That's the exact thing what I said, Percy an' the lads all agreed with me..."

Jimmy winked solemnly and then in a sudden rush of enthusiasm, he threw back his head and roared: "Three cheers for good ole Percy! Hip, hip."

Percy's hand jammed the outburst back down Jimmy's throat. "For God's sake, Jimmy," he pleaded earnestly, "will ye shut your gob. The whole bog'll hear ye."

"Don't care a shag about the whole bog," spluttered Jimmy. He started hammering on Daly's corrugated iron gate with his fist. "We want Percy! We want Percy . . . "

Percy looked around him in helpless embarrassment. And then his heart stopped as a rolling, rotund figure in blue appeared around the corner at the far end of the street.

"Jimmy, Jimmy," Percy pleaded, "for God's sake man, will ye shut up, ye'll have us both arrested. 'Tis Donovan himself . . . "

Jimmy paused for a second, cocked his head to one side like an inquisitive robin, his cloudy eyes trying to focus on the approaching Guard. He nodded once as if to confirm the fact that it was, indeed, none other than Guard O'Donovan. Then he sent a ringing call across the bog and beyond.

"Down with Donovan! We don't want Donovan! We want Percy for landlord." The Guard was close now. Percy grasped at his cheering fan and gagged him to mumbling silence.

"And down where do we want Donovan then?" The guardian of law and order, massive, stood swaying backwards and forwards, heel to toe, toe to heel. Sarcasm edged his tongue. "Hannigan, eh?" he grunted. "Drunk as usual." His small eyes transfixed Percy. "And owld Percy Murphy, no less." The emphasis on the word 'owld' was a pointed barb. "Drunk. Disorderly. Incapable, the both of ye! Well, well, well . . . "

Jimmy lurched from Percy's detaining grasp. He focused his gaze on Guard O'Donovan. O'Donovan swayed backward; Jimmy swayed forward.

"Donovan, eh?" Jimmy mimicked the Guard's sarcastic tones. "Guard O'Donovan, no less. The pot-bellied bostoon from out of the arsehole of Cork . . . "

His voice died as Percy jerked at him. "Arra, don't mind him, Guard O'Donovan!" Percy pleaded. "He must have got a drop of bad stuff somewhere but we'll be off home right away and he'll be quiet . . . "

Jimmy broke loose and tried to throw off his jacket.

"I'll whup him!" The light of battle, brightened by drunken tears of indignation, lit up his eyes. "Let me at him – I'll bate the livin' daylights outa him, I tell ye . . ."

Heads were appearing at doorways. The customers from Daly's pub came out and gathered in awed silence. Percy stuck by Jimmy, trying to calm him. The Guard's pedigree was called into question in ringing tones. Guard O'Donovan's face took on a bright red hue. His mouth gaped open and closed again. At last he found his voice. It erupted from him like surging lava bursting out of the bowels of a destroying volcano.

"Get him out of here before I lock him up," he snarled. "Get him out of me sight. Take him back to his lodgings . . . " He grabbed Jimmy by the scruff of his neck, his voice ringing in his anger.

"And start looking for new lodgings, d'ye hear me, boy? Get out of that house ye're in, for if ye're not out when I take charge of it, you and your drunken likes'll be out on yer ear in the street, d'ye understand me, boy? I'll have that house respectable. I'll have that house dacent. And furthermore..."

"And furthermore, Guard O'Donovan, I'll thank you to keep your insulting mouth shut!" The female voice behind them was a rush of angry indignation. Guard O'Donovan swung around, his mouth dropping open in complete negation of Matilda's barbed request. And Matilda McArdle herself, arms akimbo, the light of battle in her eyes, measured him with a fiery glance.

"Respectable house, indeed! You'll make MY house respectable, will you? You'll make my house decent, will you? How dare you! The very idea! And how dare you bandy my name in public and insinuate that for one moment I'd even consider marrying the likes of you...!"

"But Matilda . . . Mrs McArdle... Maam..." Guard O'Donovan's protests were swept aside. Matilda flounced past him to where Percy was supporting the wilting Jimmy, her eyes smiling sweetly.

"You poor, poor boys," she simpered, "being bullied by that awful person. Wasn't it a good job I came down to see after the rashers?"

But it wasn't Jimmy or the rashers or even Guard O'Donovan that Percy was thinking about just then. There was a sudden new light of promise in Matilda's eyes when she smiled at him – a light like the harvest moon turning a bog-hole into a sparkling pool of gold, a light like – but what does it matter? If it wasn't exactly a pool of gold, then it was a pool that would hold every penny of 336 quid in it every week.

And, as Percy is forever pointing out to his lodgers nowadays, "in affairs of the heart 'tis not money but only love that counts." At the end of the day, he warns them, when all is said and done: "shure there's nothing to bate a good love match, after all."

THE STRIKE AT BANDON'S WALL

The Irish Times, September 1986

Strikes and lockouts are not the product of twentieth century social unrest; they were with us long before James Larkin rallied the workers of Dublin to the banner of militant socialism. Look at what happened when the walls of Bandon were being constructed way back in 1610.

The walls of Bandon were to be built mainly of heavy black slate about nine feet thick and varying in height from 30 to 50 feet. The area of town enclosed was estimated at 26 English acres. There were three castles to be erected, each containing 26 rooms, the turrets and flanks to be platformed with lead and mounted with cannon.

This then was the ambitious building project about to be undertaken by Lord Cork when a militant leader of the workforce upset his programme by demanding an immediate increase in the masons' wages from two and a half pence to three pence a day.

"My members have been exploited for too long", the masons' leader told a very irate Lord Cork. "And no walls will guard the town of Bandon unless the just demands of the workers are conceded."

The Lord refused to be blackmailed by such idle varlets and he told them so in no uncertain terms. They could, he went on "betake themselves to the devil out of Bandon and, by gad, he'd be damned in Hell before he'd bow before their impudent demands." Lord Cork withdrew to his stately home and the masons marched off the site.

As in all labour disputes, there were side issues. One unfortunate mason with a sick wife and a family to support decided that he couldn't afford to join the strike and asked that he be allowed to work on alone. Lord Cork, hoping that his good example would influence the others, agreed.

Days passed into weeks. Whatever about the pressures of hunger and misery on the idle masons, the political pressures brought to bear on Lord Cork to complete the defences of Bandon became unbearable. Suddenly he pocketed his pride and capitulated, agreeing to all the demands of the striking workers. They marched triumphantly to the site and started work at the new rate – three pence a day.

As for the blackleg mason, his fellow craftsmen demanded that he be instantly dismissed but, to his credit, Lord Cork refused. That evening, however, the masons gathered menacingly around their erstwhile workmate and one of them, chosen by lot, hit him from behind with a pickaxe, splitting his skull and killing him instantly. They buried his body in the foundations of the walls and laid a course of masonry over it to conceal their crime forever from the eyes of man. They nearly succeeded.

Two hundred years later workers removing part of the old town walls came across a large flagstone. A quick tap of a pickaxe gave off a hollow sound. Visions of Spanish doubloons and buried treasures rose before their eyes, but further investigation uncovered only the mouldering bones of the unfortunate mason. His hammer and trowel lay under his broken skull as they had been placed the day the strike at Bandon's Wall had finished. And soon that was all that remained – the skeleton upon being exposed to air, crumbled into dust.

THE ETERNAL WAR

Irish Independent, March 1978

Shalom, the traditional greeting of peace still rings hollow in the streets of Israel, despite the euphoria of Camp David and President Carter's efforts to bring a peace treaty to finality. In Syria, Jordan and Lebanon the threatening sabres have never ceased to rattle, and now Ayatollah Khomeini of Iran has fanned to new fanatical flames the eternal dreams of every Arab – the re-establishment of a mighty Moslem Empire, with the cursed Jews swept forever back into the sea.

Within the sovereign state of Israel itself, Jew and Arab stand side-by-side, equal men in the eyes of the law, citizens all. But there are Jewish towns and Arab towns, Jewish sectors and Arab sectors, and everywhere a vague ghetto air of tension and distrust. At the root of the complex problem is the fact that the Arab nations regard the very existence of Israel in their midst as a symbol of their inability to overcome their own cultural short-comings, and recover their past historic glory.

For three decades, all Arab countries have refused to recognise Israel's right to exist, and Israel has had to fight five bloody wars – in fact, one long war with uneasy lulls between battles in order to survive. To the proud Arab, Israel constitutes a living reproach. That a small army of Jews could defeat the Arab armies, drawn from a vast population of 125 million people, is a bitter pill to swallow. To be asked to accept that the wandering Jews are now an integrated nation in their midst, with living standards higher than their own, is a humiliation too great to bear.

A young Arab student to whom I spoke was fiercely partisan in his views. "We Palestinians would not come to your country to try to set up a Palestinian state there. Why should the Jews come here to set up a Jewish state?"

When I suggested that Palestine was the historic Land of Israel promised to Jacob and his descendants, and in modern days, under the League of Nations Mandate, the place where the Jewish national home was to be established, he conceded a little: "But of course the Jews who were born in Palestine are entitled to live here," he agreed.

"They are Palestinians like us. But we will not tolerate Jews from Russia or Germany or America or Ireland or anywhere else. They are foreigners. They are not Palestinians and they have no right to be here."

Joseph, an Arab grocer and a Christian in his late seventies, epitomised more acceptably the less militant Arab view. Equally proud of his Arab culture, there was always a mixture of sadness and bitterness in his voice as he traced the history of Palestine over a period of 3,000 years. Scribbling maps and statistics and dates on a table napkin, he covered 3,000 years of war and riot, blood and misery from the year 1250 BC when Joshua crossed the Jordan to conquer the Lands of Canaan, to 1947 when the British mandate expired, and the Jewish National Council declared the independent State of Israel.

"The Jews have never ruled this land," he insisted. "It has been ruled by Greeks, Persians, Romans, Turks and by the British, but never by the Jews. Why should they declare it a Jewish state now?" When I pointed, out that it was not just a Jewish state, that he and a million other Arabs were citizens of this state, with full rights, he shook his head in disagreement.

"I am an old man now" he said, "and they can do no more to me. Yes, I am a full citizen, and I pay my full taxes, but I am discriminated against in housing, education, grants and in every sector of my life. I was born and lived and was married in Tiberius. After the 1947 war the 15,000 Arabs who lived there were transported to Nazareth and dumped on the side of the street. Had we no rights with our property confiscated and no place to go? Tiberius is an all-Jewish town now – no Arabs. All that Arab property confiscated. And this has happened in many places. The Jews were good people before 1947. I was always very friendly with them and we got on well. I was reproached by Arabs who referred to me as 'Joseph the Jew,' but after 1947 everything changed. When they took charge, they became different people. We wanted to work with them. We wanted nothing to do with Jordan or Syria or Egypt. We are Arabs, but we are Palestinians first, and we wanted to stay there, but they drove us out."

The Jewish businessman in Tel Aviv's Hilton Hotel did not agree. "We didn't drive out the Arabs," he emphasised very positively. "I was living in Haifa in 1947 and the Arab countries surrounding us broadcast to the Arabs of Israel urging them to quit the country because the combined Arab armies were about to drive the Jews into the sea, and it was clearly hinted that any Arabs who remained and accepted Jewish protection would be regarded as renegades. When they failed to drive us into the sea, they also reneged on their promises to the refugees. All the governments, Syria, Jordan, Lebanon and Egypt, they have kept those refugees in squalor isolated from Arab society. Thousands of men, women and children, born long after the establishment of Israel, continue to subsist in those camps. They have never even set foot in

Palestine, but they are now the terrorists that will drive us into the sea. No, don't blame us Jews. Blame the Arabs for their own troubles. We have brought nothing but prosperity to this lovely land."

Today Israel is, without doubt, a land flowing with milk and honey. Jewish enterprise and know-how have harnessed Israel's water supply. The precious water is pumped up from the Sea of Galilee and flows through 108" diameter pipes along the Mediterranean coastal plain to the southern Negev where it irrigates vast tracts of desert. Israel is now utilising over 90 per cent of her water resources and this has permitted an increase of her area under irrigation from a mere 75,000 acres in 1948 to 470,000 acres in 1978. The arid deserts of the Holy Moslem Empire are being pushed back more and more.

To the unpractised Irish eye Jew and Arab look very much alike, both races descended from the sons of Noah, both strong, both fearless, both born out of repression and rebellion, and like us Irish, cursed with the gift of a memory that will stretch back effortlessly over thousands of years. Palestinian Liberation Organisation leader, Yasser Arafat, boasts proudly: "We freed Iran today, and under the leadership of Ayatollah Khomeini and with the help of Iranian freedom fighters, we will free Palestine too and make it part of a mighty Moslem Empire."

But I keep remembering the young Arab student in Jerusalem and the old Arab grocer in Nazareth. They, too, felt at war – but only with those alien influences, be they Arab or Jewish, that sought to prevent the creation of a nation undivided, unpartitioned, not Arabic, not Jewish, but Palestinian. They were Palestinians, and they didn't want to be part of anybody's empire, political or religious. Who represents their point of view at the peace-table? Will their voices remain unheard till they too take to the streets either as freedom fighters or terrorists?

And to Irish ears does not all this have a too-familiar ring? In the years to come will Camp David be remembered like the ill-fated Sunningdale Agreement or worse, the Anglo-Irish Treaty of 1921? Only time will tell and in the land of Israel where scars are deep and a thousand years is as the blink of an eye, we may well have to wait a long, long time to find out.

THE ACCIDENT

Cork Weekly Examiner, July 1950

Oh dear, oh dearie me! Mr McCarthy felt dazed – quite dazed. If only he could remember exactly what happened! He sat down heavily on the kerb beside the wrecked Morris Minor and put his head on his chest. For 40 years he had driven cars, slow cars and fast cars – well, mostly slow cars, but the odd fast car too – why, he had owned one of the very first of those Volkswagens and they were fairly nippy – and he'd never had an accident before, not even a slight mishap.

His muddled mind tried to recall the events leading up to this catastrophe. Let's see now, he had been to early Mass as usual and then there was those two pints of Guinness in the Railway Bar with his old pal, Jack Hayes. And a couple of small ones too, of course, in between, he remembered that much. Bloody Hell, blast Jack anyhow, he hadn't really wanted to drink the small ones, but Jack just kept on and on ordering more. Not that two pints meant anything, of course, nor the couple of small ones either for that matter – they were small ones, weren't they – nobody could ever say that Tom McCarthy couldn't handle that lot? He could handle twice that any day and still be capable of driving a car.

He shook his head from side to side trying to clear the fog that cloaked the events prior to and during the accident. Yes, he could remember coming down Church Street and stopping at the traffic lights. When they turned green he crossed through the junction, up past the shops to the corner. That's when it happened. Oh dear, yes, he remembered that he was doing a nice steady 30 when some fool came dashing out of a shop straight onto the road. There had been a scream of protesting rubber when he jammed on the brakes – good job he'd had those brakes seen to only last week. Nobody was going to be able to say that Tom McCarthy didn't keep his car in excellent condition, that's for sure!

His heart sank then. That scream! Maybe, he thought hopefully, it had come from the skidding tyres – the brakes were so good, you see. God, had he hit your man, the fellow who came running out of the shop? He recalled an awful thump – an ominous, dull, 'giving' sort of thump, and then the terrific crash. He felt gingerly at his legs and his head, and up and down each arm. He appeared to be all right, thanks be to God – no broken bones, no blood anywhere. But he ought to look around – help the victim.

Oh dear me! A cold shudder rippled through him at the thought of a victim and visions of an inquest floated before him. Manslaughter! That couple of pints of Guinness could very well convict him. He, Mr Thomas McCarthy, a drunken driver! He felt too weak to move. After all those years of safe, careful driving to finish up like this. Oh dear, oh dear and the Volkswagen had never had so much as a scratch on it when he traded it in and they were as nippy a car as you could buy in their day...

A chilling thought struck him. Whatever would Maura say? How would she take it? She had always been so proud of their 'good name', so careful of it. And the neighbours – oh dear, there would be plenty of gossip there. He could hear the whispers already. That Mr McCarthy fellow – so quiet he always pretended to be, butter wouldn't melt in his mouth, oh no, and he was drunk as a Lord in that car of his. A menace on the roads, a drunken menace, that's all he was, and despite all the warnings about drunken driving. Oh, he was a funny sort was Mr McCarthy. Wouldn't be surprised if herself could down a few too – always so high and mighty were the McCarthys. Yes, they were a sanctimonious crowd!

A groan of self-pity shook him. But it was all too late now – no use sitting here brooding over it. He might as well go and find out the worst. How could this ever have happened to him of all people?

An ambulance and a police car screamed to a halt. A silent crowd had gathered but paid no attention to the lonely figure sitting woefully on the kerb. But soon enough the questions would come – the accusations. It would be better if he didn't mention the drinking. But of course they'd find out – they had their methods. Oh dear, yes, they had their methods. There would be blood tests and urine tests and it wouldn't matter a damn what Jack Hayes said – they'd have it all down there in scientific black and white.

"Hello there. You were driving the Morris Minor, weren't you?" The man sat down beside him. He didn't look like a Garda officer but you couldn't be sure of these things. Mr McCarthy eyed him warily. "Some smack you hit that lamppost – it keeled over like a broken reed." The simile seemed to please him and he repeated it with relish. "Yes, indeed... like a broken reed. Still, it wasn't your fault. Some people shouldn't be allowed out on the road with a bike not to mind a lethal weapon like a car, but you handled yours beautifully. No, it definitely wasn't your fault." There was a long pause. Mr McCarthy glowed comfortably. Then: "You didn't have any drink taken, did you?"

Ah ha! So that was one of their methods. Straight up, what a crafty lot they were – sneaky bastards. To pretend to be full of sympathy and then coming out with a leading incriminating question like that while he was still shocked and dazed. Say nothing. Say nothing till you've seen a solicitor and you know what damage was done and what charges they were going to prefer against you.

"You seem pretty certain that it wasn't my fault," Mr McCarthy said. "Did you see what happened – I'm a bit hazy myself? I think I must have hit my head on the windscreen or something." He added hastily, "I did have my seatbelt fastened, mind you." He looked at his companion. "I missed him, didn't I? I mean I didn't actually hit him, did I? The bloody fool who ran out in front of me . . . " There was desperate hope in his voice.

The man eyed him for a long moment and then pointed towards the ambulance. The crowd had drawn discreetly back and Mr McCarthy focused his eyes on the scene. A stretcher was being passed through the open doors of the ambulance. There was a still limp shape under the sheet. The men in the crowd took off their hats.

Oh dear, oh dearie me. Mr McCarthy's voice trembled with emotion. "I didn't kill him, did I? But it wasn't my fault. You'll swear to that, won't you? He ran straight out in front of me without even a look to the right or the left. I never had a chance – you saw that . . . "

"Oh, I saw it alright. And don't worry – it wasn't your fault. Nobody could possibly blame you for what happened. But I'm afraid I won't be able to testify on your behalf at the inquest." Mr McCarthy looked at him in shocked appeal. The man smiled and put his arm protectively around Mr McCarthy's shoulder. "Don't you see? I'm the fella you killed . . . "

Mr McCarthy shrunk back, his eyes wide with horror

and fright. Oh God, he was obviously going mad – all the drink and the bang on his head and the shock – it was all getting to him. The arm tightened around his shoulders and a calming voice spoke reassuringly in his ear.

"Come along, my friend – bear up. No use taking it so hard. Everything will be all right. And, anyway, it's high time you reported to someone, you know. You can't just hang around here like this."

Yes, yes, of course! Mr McCarthy was on his feet immediately, willing and anxious to do the right thing. "A garda or a doctor, where are they all?"

The hand on his shoulder detained him. "Look here, my friend, you don't seem to appreciate what's going on. It's no use going to a garda or a doctor." The voice was gentle, like a mother reproving an errant son. "Don't you see? You're dead too. Look!"

And Mr McCarthy saw his own body being passed into the ambulance. Arm in arm, he and his victim walked away. Oh dear, oh dearie me...

THE HEALING WATERS

Cork Hollybough, December 1953

It was my fault, I was the doctor and I should have told John McNaughton that first evening that his longed-for son had been born a cripple. But I wasn't all that long qualified. I was inexperienced, not very sure of myself.

Somehow I felt it the moment I examined the frail, screaming newborn boy – something was wrong. His left leg, his left arm, his whole left side – it just wasn't quite... quite normal. I searched my memory frantically for reasons, for words to express them, but nothing came – only vague harassing doubts.

The midwife? She was a friend of the family. She knew how John McNaughton had longed, all these years, for a son and heir, and maybe she was blinded by the happy, wistful smile of exhausted triumph on Mary McNaughton's face. She noticed nothing and I, God forgive me, kept silent.

John McNaughton was beside himself with delight. "Lord love me," he chuckled happily, "a son at last, eh! A young McNaughton!" He went over again to the cot and gazed adoringly down at the little puckered face. "Seven pounds of good McNaughton flesh!" He chucked the baby lightly under the chin with his huge ham of a fist. "Grow up fast, boy!" he said with a caressing gentleness you'd hardly expect from such a big man. "You and I have lots and lots to do!"

That stirred something inside me. "Mr McNaughton" I started, but John didn't give me a chance.

"Come on, downstairs, doctor," he interrupted. "Let's have a drink. You've done a great job tonight and I appreciate it." And with an almost shy, tender smile to his wife, he led the way out of the room, his happy, bellowing laughter soothing the pricking of my medically inexperienced conscience. I looked from the baby to Mrs McNaughton. She smiled a slow, tremulous smile. There was a strange new loveliness in her tired face. It was obvious that she felt that this was a fresh start in her life with her husband. Her eyes shone with joyous pathetic anticipation. Her trembling lips said to me, "Thank you doctor. Thank you ever so much". God, how utterly inadequate I felt then.

John McNaughton was the most successful farmer in our area. His sprawling acres of rich land were models of modern farming miracles. Fat, sleek cattle grazed on lush, green grass. Heavy corn waved in fleeting shadows of green and gold. Everywhere was fruitful prosperity. John McNaughton had everything – so said his neighbours. Marrying Mary had made a man of him, they said.

Father McHugh had often told me about the wedding day. It was a milestone in the life of the community. Things happened "before John McNaughton got married" or "after John McNaughton got married." There was dancing and drinking and merriment. Mary was so small and so beautiful beside the tall, handsome, rich John. Mary was so happy and carefree, moving into her new home, bringing brightness and colour to the drabness of an all-male farmhouse.

And John made no secret of his new happiness. Neither did he make any secret of his ambition. He hoped for a son to carry on the McNaughton tradition. He needed that son. But, as the barren years went by, the light went out of Mary's eyes with the growing knowledge that, somehow, she had failed her perplexed husband. And John growing morose and sour and unloving, losing his friends and his good name, turning once more to drink in his bewildered unhappiness.

Soon the people were saying, some pityingly, some spitefully: "The McNaughtons have everything – everything except what they want . . . "

But now, at last, all that was changed. Big John's huge frame trembled with the joy of it. He handed me a tumbler of whiskey. "To my son, Francis John McNaughton," he toasted, clinking his glass against mine. He threw out his barrel-like chest, the muscles in his arms and neck expanding proudly, and I could see in his eyes that he was thinking of the days ahead, when this son, now so tiny and helpless upstairs, would be a man like himself, healthy in mind and limb, a true farmer of the McNaughton breed.

"To the day when my son takes over this farm!" I swallowed painfully and tried to banish the lurking doubts from my mind. Maybe I was wrong, I told myself. It was too early to make a definite diagnosis. My very inexperience was the root of my doubts.

"To Francis John McNaughton!" I toasted. But I couldn't offer any more. The words stuck in my throat. And the sound of a car's wheels squealing to a stop outside relieved what was beginning to be a trying situation.

Before the car was properly stopped, we knew it was our parish priest, Father McHugh. His laughing voice demanded from everybody within earshot if it was true that his old friend had been blessed with a son. John swelled with the pride of it. Then the priest was in the kitchen, his lean face alight with eager delight; his swinging cassock betraying the haste with which he had rushed over from the church on hearing the news.

"Congratulations, John!" he grinned good-naturedly. "I hear you've got yourself an heir!" John was already filling out another tumbler. "True enough, Father!" he smiled proudly, trying to restrain the surging pride inside him. "Seven pounds and he as like me as ever a boy was like his father!"

Fr McHugh, finishing wringing the strong brown hand, raised his glass in another toast. I refused a refill and made some excuse about going up to see to the mother's comfort, but I paused above on the landing and listened.

"To your son, John" said Fr McHugh. "May he live long and be as good a man as his father."

Two glasses clinked and then came John's voice, happy and slightly blurred:

"Lord love me, Father, that boy has made me the proudest man in the world this day!"

I could feel the moist sweat on the palms of my hands as my doubts surged up to overwhelm me. The happiest man in the world this day! The words stuck in my mind then, and I think they must have stuck in Fr McHugh's mind too, because 12 long dreadful years later he repeated them to John McNaughton – but this time his voice held an undercurrent of bitterness and sympathy, anger and sorrow, all jumbled together.

* * * *

The three of us, Fr McHugh, John and myself, were driving back up to John's place after a day's shooting. It had been a successful day and we were in the best of spirits. But, just as we turned up into the drive, came calamity. Francis, now a frail, delicate boy of twelve, came limping out eagerly through a break in the hedge, and almost fell under the wheels of the car. It was pathetic to

see the little twisted body trying to control itself. He was
waving his right arm. His left arm lay limply at his side.
It had never moved since the day he was born. His pale,
beautiful face, with its two rosy cheeks and large expressive,
intelligent eyes, was alight with welcome. He had
recognised Fr McHugh's car, but not till now had he
realised that his father was also in it.

It was heart-rending to see the instant change that
came over him. The happy light fled from his face as a
cloud sweeps the silver from the smooth waters of a lake.
He tried to draw back to hide. My heart, hardened by
years of medical practice, went out to him then. The
superhuman effort to control his semi-paralysed body
failed. He stumbled helplessly and fell in an awkward
bundle. I saw tears of angry frustration well into those
brown eyes. I saw the innate McNaughton pride struggle
and fail. And then his mother, never far from him, came
dashing out from the field beyond to gather him
protectively into her arms. Her eyes too held anger and
fear and apology. And John McNaughton? From where I
sat in the back seat I saw his neck redden with embarrassed
anger.

"Mary," he said tightly through the window, "can you
not keep that cripple in the house?" And then he sat
stiffly, staring straight ahead, waiting for Fr McHugh to
drive on.

The cool silence of the evening was unbroken for long
embarrassing seconds. Mary faltered, two red spots
burning her cheeks, and then, without another glance at
us, she vanished through the hedge, Francis clutched to
her breast. John made a throaty, impatient grunt. And at
last, Fr McHugh spoke, his deep voice vibrant with the
emotion that surged in him.

"May God forgive you, John McNaughton for what

you said just now! May He close his ears to it and not hold it against you!" His trembling hand fell heavily on John's hunched shoulder. "Do you remember the day he was born? Do you, man? Twelve short years ago? Do you remember what you said to me then? You said that boy made you the proudest man in the whole wide world! The proudest man in the whole wide world!" The bitterness crept out of the priest's voice.

"And if God in His wisdom saw fit not to give him the full use of his limbs, is that reason for you to refer to him as you did just now in the presence of his mother, to refer to him as a cripple?" He pulled John around to him to make him face him. "Is it?" he demanded angrily. "Is it?"

John made a sulky effort to open the door of the car and get out, but Fr McHugh restrained him. I kept silent, those guilty doubts of 12 years before stabbing me. In a way I felt that I, because of my silence that night long ago, had contributed greatly to John's bitter attitude. I knew so well what was going on in his mind. Twenty times at least in the last 12 years, when specialist after specialist had shaken his head over Francis's twisted body, John had poured out his grief in my surgery. Now when at last he managed to speak his voice was broken.

"I-I'm sorry, Father," he groaned, "God be my witness, I'm sorry. I've tried to love him. I've tried to be a father to him, but – oh my God, the years and years I pined for a son. The hours I spent in the chapel praying! Mary and myself – and then . . . " His voice choked in his throat. "And then He gave us a cripple, for that's all he is. God bless the mark, a helpless cripple."

The knuckles of Fr McHugh's hands showed white under the skin. The throbbing intensity in his voice tried desperately to break through the prejudiced grief of his old friend.

"But, 'tis God's will! Don't you see? You must accept it. It's hard. I know, but 'tis His will!" His fist was beating a tattoo on John's shoulder as if he were trying to beat in the message by physical force. "If He wanted him whole, Francis would be whole. There's a reason, don't you realise, for everything He does. If He willed it the boy would be alright and . . . "

"But the doctors!" John interrupted bitterly. "The doctors, specialists, they all say his case is hopeless. They say that he'll –"

"Oh, blast the doctors!" shouted Fr McHugh irreverently. "They're only human beings! It's God's will that counts. If He wanted Francis to stay like this, he'll stay. But if He decides otherwise . . . "

His voice slowly trailed away. Even I, in the back seat, felt the change that suddenly swept over John McNaughton. A surprised light of incredulous anticipation lit his haggard face. He swung around and looked at me and then back to Fr McHugh.

"Good God!" he whispered. "Why didn't I never think of this before? What blinded me?" He smashed a fist into the palm of his other hand. "Lourdes! That's the place! I'll take him there. He'll be cured there." The complete conviction in his tones was awe-inspiring. He hadn't a doubt about it in his mind. "I know it!" he whispered almost to himself. "I can feel it now. "

He threw open the door and was gone without another glance at us. Off down through the orchard he ran, his voice shrill with his new excitement.

"Mary!" he called. "Mary! Francis! Where are ye?"

Fr McHugh had made an effort to follow him. Now he got back into the car. There was bewilderment on his face as he slumped into the seat behind the wheel,

"God forgive me, what have I done at all, at all!" he mumbled to himself. My eyes widened in surprise.

"Why, my dear Father," I congratulated, "what have you done except to give him new hope . . . " But the look the priest gave me stopped me short.

"Hope!" he smiled bitterly. "I've given him hope! Rather have I ruined him?" He turned slowly around to me. "Don't you see? He's going to Lourdes in the wrong spirit. His attitude is wrong. 'Here's my crippled son! Cure him', that's his attitude. And if God in His wisdom doesn't see fit to cure him . . . "

I made no comment, I couldn't. I saw Fr McHugh's point only too clearly. If Francis wasn't cured at Lourdes then John McNaughton would have another grudge against the world and against his God. And big John McNaughton wasn't the type of man who forgot or forgave those against whom he bore a grudge . . .

The sinking sun fell below the rim of the distant mountains. It felt very cold as we drove back to the village.

* * * *

It was six weeks later when I drove up to the farm again. Mary had rung me. She hadn't been sleeping very well, she said. Since John and Francis had gone to Lourdes she had hardly slept a wink. They were due back this evening. She'd not heard a word from them – not even a card. Would I come up? About seven o'clock. That's when they were due home.

We were together in the kitchen when they arrived. I had tried to get her to go to bed but she refused.

"I want to be here when Francis gets back," she told me in a stricken whisper. "I – I – God knows how John has been treating the poor child – especially when he realised . . . " Her voice faded in a throaty sob. I didn't know what to say. I couldn't find words to express how I felt, what I hoped.

"You don't expect that Francis – that the visit to Lourdes will have any result?" I said, at last.

Mary's big, bright eyes met mine. She shook her head slowly. "No, doctor," she whispered. "Father McHugh is right. John's attitude isn't the right one. He . . . "

She left it at that. Away in the distance we could hear a car. Then twin shafts of light bit through the darkness, bathing the gaunt hedges in yellow and gold. I tried to avoid her eyes. I could see her trembling. I squeezed her arm encouragingly. She smiled then.

"I'll be all right, doctor." And I knew that she would be. My own heart was beginning to pound. The car stopped outside.

"You go on out, please," said Mary, blowing her nose briskly. "I think I'd prefer to meet them in here." I nodded and hurried out

John was already out of the car. He swung around when I opened the kitchen door. His beaming smile took be by surprise.

"Why, hello there, Doc!" Then the smile fled from his face. "Mary? Is Mary all right?" I nodded reassuringly, my heart doing strange, funny things inside me. I hadn't seen John McNaughton so happy since... since . . . Could Francis have been cured, I wondered hopefully. Could it be that? But my hopes came tumbling down when John, smiling again, opened the passenger door and helped Francis out. His twisted body was the same. There was no change in him. No change, I realised suddenly, except that his face was alight with healthy, boyish happiness – happiness I had never seen in him before when his father was around!

"Hello, doctor," he smiled shyly, holding out his hand politely. I shook it heartily.

"How did you like it in France?" I asked, still struggling with the doubts inside me. I could feel rather than see that Mary had followed me out that she was standing just inside the door. Francis didn't get a chance to answer

"Lord love me, doc, 'twas a great experience," put in John. There was a strange humility in his voice, a new, deep, alien humility. He was getting the cases out of the car. "All those poor invalids there, thousands of them and they so – so patient, and expectant . . . " He shook his head slowly, at a loss for words. Then the old laughter boomed out in his voice.

"And the way our Francis here got along with them French fellows – he was a great help to everybody." John had his arm around the boy's shoulders. "Did you know he could speak French, eh? And fluently at that! Learnt it from Father McHugh, he did! And to think I never knew!"

I was amazed at the pride in his voice as he gazed down adoringly at the little boy beside him. Then Mary came rushing out. Never had I seen her so beautiful. For long, silent, blissful seconds, her eyes locked with John's. Then Francis was in her arms and they were crying and laughing, and laughing and crying. And I slipped away into the dark. They didn't need me there.

The night sky, a hanging canopy of star-studded velvet, stretched above me. I stood and I looked into it and I felt small and inadequate and amazed at the wonder of it all.

"Mother of God," I whispered, in awed reverence, "You cured John McNaughton! He bathed in the healing waters and you cured him."

And I felt all full up inside... choked. God's will had been done. And it had been done in His own mysterious fashion and in His own inexplicable way.

THE WOMAN WHO WAITED

Radio Eireann, December 1952

'The Haven' is going to be demolished. I read about it today in the old hometown newspaper. It must be well over 60 years since I last saw that gaunt, bleak old house standing atop the cliffs, eerie and alone, bravely defying the greedy seas and the raging storms that swept it. And now they're going to pull it down.

Miss Belinda won't like that. And the Captain, he won't like it either. Wherever in land or sea his body is lying, I know his spirit will be up there on the cliffs with Belinda's as stone is torn from protesting stone. Miss Belinda herself is in the little graveyard outside the village. We buried her there that Christmas time 70 long years ago.

It's hard to realise that it wasn't yesterday it all happened – time slips by quickly when you pass the half way mark, and I was only a boy at the time. But I'll never forget. The memory of that Christmas time has been locked inside me down the years and I never, ever told a soul. I was afraid that the people in the village would say that I was batty too. That's what they said about Belinda – Batty Belinda they called her. If the children were very naughty, their mothers would threaten that they'd be sent up to stay at Batty Belinda's house and that would quieten them. They were all afraid of her – everybody that is, except me.

I liked Miss Belinda, and she liked me. She came to the village every Sunday to go to Mass, and I was the only person she ever spoke to. I was also the only person ever allowed inside her rambling, creepy old house. And I was never, never, afraid – not until that Christmas Day when I found her body. She was all cold and stiff, and she was wearing her wedding dress . . .

I wasn't terribly afraid then either, only maybe for a few minutes – until I realised what had happened. After that, I was, well, sort of pleased – pleased that it had all turned out just like Miss Belinda said it would. I was so young then, you see, and like her, I didn't mix well with other people. That probably helped to create the strange affectionate bond that existed between Miss Belinda and myself.

She'd say to me: "You're a good lad, Jack. You're the sort of son I'd have liked if . . . if . . . " and her quavering voice would trail off, and she'd look out across the grumbling, restless sea tearing at the foot of the cliffs below, tearing, pounding, demanding, always demanding, as if still not satisfied with all it had stolen from Miss Belinda . . .

And I'd sit there, silent and quiet, watching her stricken blue eyes glistening with tears, and feeling her trembling of the long, bony fingers on my shoulder. Then, after a minute or so, she'd get up and glide away without another word to me, and I'd slip out the back way with the empty basket.

Every Thursday it was that I'd go up to her with the groceries. My father owned the shop in the village and he didn't like it if I stayed too long on the cliffs. He'd say: "Run up to the Haven with the stuff, Jack, and hurry back, now, d'hear me, boy? No hanging about there talking to Batty Belinda or she'll have you as batty as herself with her lights and her rubbishy talk . . . "

I didn't tell you about the lights, did I? Every night she'd put a lighted candle in every window facing out to the sea. It looked just like Christmas in her house every night of the year as soon as the darkness thickened a bit. One by one, you'd see the lights flicker up till the whole skull of the house had six shining eyes, all of them looking out across the sea. And somewhere in the gloom you could be sure that there were two more eager eyes, moist and shining, watching and waiting – always waiting, and always moist. Miss Belinda was waiting for the Captain to come sailing home to marry her.

She was quite certain that he'd come back for her some day – and after 40 years of lonely waiting too! Of course everybody in the village said that his ship had been lost at sea, or that he'd met one of those queer foreign woman and married her. You know what these sailors are like, they'd say, and they'd nudge one another and shake their heads knowingly. It was all very sad, of course, because the Captain was supposed to marry Miss Belinda when he came back from that last voyage. But there you are, it was batty to think that he'd turn up after 40 years and marry her. That's what they said in the village.

Miss Belinda didn't think that though. Oh no! She knew! She showed me her wedding dress one day. She took me upstairs and opened the old oak chest and lifted out the glittering, shimmering satin gown, and held it up to her thin body. "It's getting a bit big for me," she whispered almost to herself. "But I'll be able to put a tuck in it when I need it. It's what he'd want me to wear when he gets back . . . "

I could barely hear the words because the desperate whisper was trembling and broken. "He said he'd come back. He said he'd come back and take me away from this place, and he will. He will. I know he will. And I'll wear this gown just like I was going to wear it 40 years ago..."

Then she put the dress back in the chest and walked down the long corridor to her room – she had forgotten that I was ever with her. But despite the things they said in the village, I felt sure that there was something more than mere hope throbbing inside her breast. She was certain, absolutely certain. The Captain had promised, and she was waiting. I was very young, but I felt sure that the Captain would keep his promise – some day – somehow!

He did, too! It was the very following Christmas. When I took up the groceries on the Thursday, she said to me: "Come up to see me on Christmas Eve, Jack, and I'll have something nice for you."

We were very busy in the shop that Christmas Eve but when we finished I managed to slip away without my father seeing me. The snow was swirling down, biting and flashing in the wind that swept in across the sea. There was no moon that night and it was cold and creepy and dark on the cliffs, but I wasn't worried. I knew every inch of the way.

I was almost there when I noticed something strange: except for one room on the ground floor, the Haven was in darkness. That puzzled me and I stopped for a minute to consider it. As long as I could remember, I had never known a night that those six little lights weren't winking hopefully out through the dark.

A worried spark kindled inside me but I quenched it. There was that one light, I pointed out to myself. Perhaps Miss Belinda hadn't had time to light the others. Perhaps she needed some help with them. Yes, that was it. I fought my way against the wind until I came to the lighted window. And then I heard the laugh – a man's laugh! That stopped me dead. A man at the Haven I thought? No man had entered that house since the Captain sailed away, over 40 years ago. Suddenly strange hope welled up inside me. My heart pounded as I crept to the window. I scraped away the snow and I peeped.

Through the misted glass I could see the large room lit by a solitary flickering candle. Long shivering shadows played on the walls. My heart gave a joyful leap when a tall figure came between the candle and me. There could be no doubt about it. There he was, resplendent in his uniform with the shiny buttons and the four gold stripes on his cuffs, tall, handsome and immaculate. He was standing by the table turning the pages of a photograph album – Miss Belinda had often shown it to me – and he was laughing to himself. 1 watched in amazement and delight. My heart was singing with happiness for Miss Belinda. She had been right all the time. He had come back. After all the years of waiting patiently, her Captain had come sailing home.

Then the door opened and I saw Miss Belinda. The sight of her took my breath away as she stood there framed in the doorway, a happy contented smile lighting her face. The satin gown reflected the flickering candlelight and a wondrous beauty had banished the lonely sadness from her eyes forever. Her face radiated happiness and adoration. The man she had waited for was back. She walked slowly, proudly to him. His arm went possessively about her. They were together at last and I knew that he'd never, never leave her again.

My teeth were chattering with the cold but I felt warm and cosy inside. Oh, I was so happy for Miss Belinda. I watched them for a few minutes and then I slipped quietly away – I wouldn't intrude on them tonight; the Christmas present she promised me could wait. I wanted so badly to get back down to the village, to shout it out that Miss Belinda's Captain was back despite all their sneers. I wanted to see the amazement on their faces when they heard my wonderful news.

I ran all the way down the path. My breath was strangling me but I shouted my news into the wind: "The Captain's back! The Captain's back!" And the raging wind picked up my words and flung them back down on the angry face of the frustrated sea.

A thought struck me when I paused for breath outside the village. This was Miss Belinda's happiest hour. It wouldn't be fair for me to tell, would it? Let her show them! Let her savour the stupid amazement on their faces when she'd arrive down to the chapel tomorrow. I could picture it all – how she'd sweep up the aisle to her usual seat, but this time she'd be on the arm of the Captain. She'd bow and she'd smile and the villagers would nudge one another and be ashamed of the things they'd being saying for the past 40 years.

And I'd be up there in the gallery looking down and glowing inside. Yes, that's how we'd do it tomorrow. We'd show them – Miss Belinda, the Captain and I! I slipped in home quietly and went to bed. But I couldn't sleep – I was much too excited.

Early next morning, I was first off to Mass – I wanted a seat right up there in the front of the gallery where I'd have a really good view. I never took my eyes off the front door.

The Mass started but there was still no sign of Miss Belinda and the Captain. But I knew exactly how she was going to enact it – she'd be just a little late, like any bride, so that everyone would see her. We came to the Gospel and there was still no sign of them. We sat down for the sermon and I began to feel vaguely worried. God forgive me, I didn't hear a word the priest said. A woman beside me gave me a vicious dig when I fidgeted but I ignored her. I made up my mind then – something had gone wrong. I slipped out of the chapel before Mass was finished and I headed for the cliffs.

The snow had stopped and I ran as hard as I could up the path to the Haven. The wind was howling and the house seemed cold and empty from the outside. The happiness of last night was gone. The back door was open and I went into the kitchen. Nobody was there, and there wasn't a sign of anyone.

"Miss Belinda! Captain!" My voice rang eerily through the house, but there wasn't a sound after the empty echoes died away. I looked in all the rooms downstairs. Nobody. I crept up the broad staircase. The old oak chest was on the landing – open and empty. I felt a little frightened then. I went along to Miss Belinda's room. The door was ajar as if somebody had just gone in. I pushed. It swung wide with a noisy creak. I peeped in. Then my breath sobbed out in utter relief – there sitting up in the bed, propped up by pillows, was Miss Belinda. She was wearing her wedding dress, and her face was fixed in that warm smile of welcome that brought back the comforting glow inside me. I hurried across to her.

"Gosh, Miss Belinda," I said, "You had me so worried there when you didn't answer . . . " My voice died in my throat. Her unblinking blue eyes were staring straight past me. They hadn't moved – just staring, staring. I reached out fearfully and touched her hand. Cold and stiff – oh, so cold! I had never seen a dead person before...

I ran from the room. "Captain! Captain," I called, "where are you?" The echo of my voice was the only reply. Out through the kitchen door, then down the cliff

path as fast as I could run. I wasn't thinking any more –
I couldn't. My mind was blank. The people were coming
out of the chapel.

"Miss Belinda's dead," I shouted. "I saw her. She's
sitting up in bed with her wedding dress on, and she's
dead . . . "

I don't know to this day why I didn't tell them about
the Captain. I suppose it was because of the stupid way
they stood and stared at me. Why should I tell them? Let
them find out for themselves. I don't know how long it
was before they got the doctor and a small group of them
started up the cliffs. I ducked around the back and followed
them. I wanted to be there when they met the Captain.
They had gone upstairs when I reached the house. I
crept up the stairs. I could hear the doctor's voice inside.
"Twenty-four hours at least. Yesterday morning early,
I'd say. She just died . . . "

Yesterday morning? I put my hand on the door to go
in, to tell him that he was wrong, that she wasn't dead all
that time, that I had seen her downstairs only last night
with the Captain. I wanted to tell them how young she
looked, how beautiful, how very different she had been.

The wind started to howl outside and a flurry of flying
snow rattled the windows. A small shiver rippled through
me. Miss Belinda had looked different last night. It was
then I think that I understood. I crept out into the snow.
The tears were cold on my face.

I never told. They'd only say that I was batty too. But
Miss Belinda knew and I knew – the Captain had promised
that he'd come and take her away, and he did. He came a
long, long way to keep that promise, and he took her a
long, long way back to where they'd be together forever.

But I knew that the people of the village wouldn't
understand. That's why I never told.

THE KIBBUTZ – ISRAEL'S CORNERSTONE

Cork Examiner, April 1979

When Arab guns range menacingly along Israel's desolate frontiers, the prime target is inevitably a lonely kibbutz peopled by zealous civilian Jews to whom the gun and the plough are equally important and equally familiar. And though the kibbutz system is not an integral part of the Israeli army structure, it is a vitally important factor in its military strategy.

Basically, the kibbutz is a place of work, but more than that, the kibbutz system embraces the whole way of life of the worker; it is a system of total collective living. It is a truly unique phenomenon in the social and political system of the modern state of Israel.

Groups of persons come together of their own free will and set up a community ruled by the majority vote of the general assembly. Each year an executive committee is elected. The top officer is the secretary. There is also a treasurer, a housekeeper and other minor officials. But the officials do not enjoy any special privileges – all the members are equal.

Degania, the first kibbutz was founded in the Jordan valley in 1910 by a group of young Russian emigrants who wanted to institute a society based on communal living, communal effort and absolute equality between members. Their own labour would provide the fruits, and those fruits would serve their own needs. And the system worked! Those young Russians, themselves fugitives from Russian injustice, successfully set up what can only be described as a true working Marxist democracy.

Their example was quickly followed and other kibbutzim were set up all over Israel, but usually in the more desolate areas facing the borders of hostile Arab nations. Exposed as they were to every danger they were very much on their own as they strove to work the inhospitable land, while at the same time defending themselves from their envious neighbours. Through force of events these communities became the strategic military outposts that felt the first impact of the Arab invasion of 1948. By their stubborn resistance and courage they absorbed and aborted that furious attack.

The modern kibbutz is still a communal village with little or no private property. The community buildings include the dining room, children's homes, the school, barns, silos and in modern days even factories or hotels. In the pioneering days, the kibbutzniks slept in dormitories or tents. Today, except for the newly admitted bachelor members, they have small one or two bed-roomed houses with bathrooms. The dining hall is the nerve centre of the kibbutz. In addition to gathering there for meals, the residents gather there for community business meetings, for entertainment and recreation. The members cook food in the communal kitchen – male or female – and all others take turns at serving. Other chores: laundry, mending of clothes, cleaning, building maintenance, and such like, are assigned by rote.

The annual budget takes in the purchase of clothing for the members, the provision of pocket money for days off, and money for an annual vacation. And all medicines, medical care and hospitalisation is provided free. In effect, the community takes on responsibility for the total needs of the members and, in return, each member gives fully and totally according to his ability. The real strength of the kibbutz lies in the fact that anybody is free to enter, stay or leave. If he stays, he works and gives of his best and in return receives food, shelter and protection. If he decides to leave he is given severance money. At the age of eighteen, all young men and women are called up for army service, and on completion of that service they may ask to be readmitted as a member of the kibbutz in which they were reared, or they may choose to go their own way in life outside the kibbutz system.

Perhaps the most startling feature of the kibbutz system is the approach to the upbringing of children. From the earliest age they live and sleep in communal homes, Trained women take care of babies, children and adolescents. Parents have their children with them for just an hour or two after work each day. This system, say the Israeli psychologists, far from driving a wedge between parent and children, actually strengthens the bonds of love and affection. The school is in the kibbutz and the children are educated to the age of eighteen. A child who shows unusual promise in any field has literally no expense spared in developing that promise. If necessary, he will be sent to and maintained in any city of the world where those talents can best be nurtured. Today there are up to 300 kibbutzim in Israel. While they account for over one third of the country's agricultural production, no longer are they all dependant on the land for their living, Some have branched out into factory and hotel business, and the kibbutz culture and influence touches nearly every sphere of business in Israel. Ein Gev, on the eastern shores of the Sea of Galilee, is a typical example of the modern kibbutz. Founded by Jews fleeing from Nazi persecution in 1937, a stark watchtower, similar to those at Auschwitz or Dachau, dominates the entrance to the kibbutz and grimly reminds members and visitors alike of the tragic holocaust that so recently enveloped the Jewish people. Farming in such a desolate area, within easy reach of Syrian guns, was never a money-making proposition, so ways and means of diversification were devised. With tourism moving into the top place in the Israeli economy, the Ein Gev kibbutz made two brilliant moves – they opened a restaurant and, at the same time, they founded the Kinneret Sailing Company to run a ferry service between the kibbutz and the thriving town of Tiberias just across the lake.

"St Peter's fish" is the speciality of the Ein Gev restaurant. A member of the perch family, it can be a little disconcerting to be faced with head, eyes, fins and tail still in place on your plate, but it is a most succulent dish and its reputation is growing, not just in Israel but all over the world. With a turnover of close on £4 million per annum, Ein Gev is a rich and thriving kibbutz. It does, of course, like any money-making concern, have to pay tax to the state, but it has not neglected its cultural responsibilities, The kibbutz has built a concert hall seating 3,000 people, and its Music and Folklore Festivals held at Easter and in the autumn, draw capacity crowds from all over Israel.

Ein Gev, self-sufficient, successful, thriving, is a microcosm of the modern Israel that is founded on the kibbutz system and, in itself, has become a tourist attraction, No wonder an official of the Ministry for Tourism described the kibbutz as Israel's Eiffel Tower!

But only a people whose spirit was tempered in the white-hot oven of fanatical persecution for over 2,000 years could freely and willingly adapt to such an unselfish way of life. The Jewish people, having come through

their holocaust, have created a way of life that is, indeed,
truly unique.

... AND IT ALL STARTED IN WEST CORK

RTÉ, *Sunday Miscellany*, June 2002

It is generally assumed in West Cork that when historians write about the saints and scholars of Ireland they are referring to the saints and scholars of West Cork. After all, it's an accepted fact down there that you couldn't look under a bush or behind a rock without coming across the remains of an abbey, a school, a holy well or something or other dedicated to one of their many local saints.

However, despite this proud heritage of piety and the centuries of unswerving loyalty to Mother Church, there is this one dark secret, this one ugly scar, which lately is pushing itself more and more to the surface in the pages of West Cork history. In 1830 there was an ungodly communist commune thriving in the picturesque village of Glandore. And that was the year when Karl Marx, the so-called founder of Communism, was only a lad of twelve. Mind you, in West Cork they were always a bit ahead of their time.

William Thompson, a wealthy landowner, set up this communist commune. Thompson was born in Rosscarbery in 1775, the son of a Cork merchant; he spent much of his early life in France and Belgium where he became exposed to the doctrines of the French revolution. He fell very much under the spell of the theories of Voltaire and soon he was regarded in Europe as a leading radical intellectual whose writings made a major contribution to the development of the early nineteenth-century co-operative movement.

On the death of his father, Thompson inherited an estate of 1,400 acres around the village of Glandore, and already having a large fortune at his disposal, he decided to go ahead with his pet project. This was, as he put it, "the establishment of a community on the principles of mutual co-operation, united possessions and equality of exertions and the means of enjoyment."

Under this co-operative system, a group of people was chosen to settle on his land, which he divided into lots of one acre per person. Each individual contributed a sum of money, from £20 to £100, depending on what he could afford, and each pursued the trade or profession for which he had been trained. Everybody worked for the common good, and each person's skills and output were available free at all times to the other members of the community. The system seemed to work very well under the general direction of Thompson and the community thrived. Unfortunately, Thompson died in 1832 at the early age of fifty-eight. In his will he left the bulk of his fortune to the community but his sister, outraged at what she regarded as the wanton dissipation of the family fortune, contested the will in law. After a long and expensive period of litigation, the court ruled in her favour and the will was declared invalid on the grounds that the property had been willed for immoral purposes.

Whatever the people of today's West Cork might think, the good citizens of 1832 who made up the jury, were not quite ready to accept what was one of the first principles of Thomson's theories – there would be no necessity for marriage within the community as wives would be shared as well as property and skills.

And so the Thompson project was quietly abandoned

and the good citizens of West Cork returned to the ways of their saints and their scholars. Years later Karl Marx adopted Thompson's pioneering development of the theory of labour values as the cornerstone of his communist thinking. In a small museum in Prague, in the Czech Republic, there is a bronze bust on display with the inscription: "Philosopher William Thompson – An Irish Socialist and forerunner of Karl Marx."

But as yet, Ireland has done nothing to mark the achievements of its communist son.

THE GENERAL'S
RAINCOAT

Irish Independent, August 1978

It was raining at 1.30 in the morning when our plane
landed in Lourdes – a steady, drenching, drizzling
downpour. And it was still streaming down eight hours
later when I made my way to the Grotto. And, of course,
I had no raincoat. Tour companies, ever anxious to sell
their holidays in the sun, never stress the need for anything
as basic as a plastic Mac when they publish their brochures
of holiday fun.

Even in the wonderful tranquillity of the Grotto it is
quite difficult to meditate meaningfully with water dripping
down your neck. After a few minutes, I abandoned all
hope of pious participation in the opening ceremony and
squelched my way back to the many shops that line the
narrow streets of Lourdes.

A charming shop assistant, tall, vivacious, dark and
slim, greeted me like a long-lost friend, her well-attuned
ears immediately identifying my Irish accent. Of course
she had a raincoat that would fit m'siu! Mon Dieu, m'siu
is such a fine man, so tall, and so like our own dear
General de Gaulle to whom she sold a similar coat just a
few months ago!

And she doesn't often meet such fine men in Lourdes,
and oh la la, how well this coat looks on m'sieu! – even
better than it had looked on General de Gaulle. She linked
my arm with easy intimacy and escorted me to a full-

length mirror. We stood like a shy, happy couple posing for our wedding photographs. She gazed up warmly into my damp face with wide-eyed Gallic charm, and I, wet and bemused at such dazzling attention, no longer thinking about raincoats – and anyway, it seemed to fit and it had a hood.

"How much do you charge?" I asked. Under the circumstances my question sounded crude. Her brown eyes were locked with mine, tempting, teasing. She ran her hands up and down the coat, moulding the folds of plastic to my body. For me, so handsome like her own dear General? – and, oh, how I loved the way her tongue tippy-toed through each syllable of her own dear Gener-al – for me, just 99 francs. I fumbled through the unfamiliar currency in my wallet. And was there anything else she could do for m'sieu? Anything? Anything?

I swallowed hard, hesitated and then, just in time, remembered that I was in the holy city of Lourdes. I put the one hundred francs note on the counter and fled back to the timeless safety of the Grotto, the rain now beating a pleasant pattering tune on the shiny protective plastic. I tried in vain to refocus my wandering thoughts, my body tall, my shoulders squared stiffly, standing as I imagined her own dear Gen-er-al would have stood. It was hours later before it dawned on me that I had paid one hundred francs for a plastic Mac that seemed to be available in every other shop for a third of that price. A seasoned Lourdes-goer warned me – too late – that not only is Lourdes a very expensive town but the shopkeepers seem to make up the prices as they go along. And the nearer you get to the Grotto, the more expensive grow the shops.

I still have the raincoat tucked away in the back of my wardrobe and I still remember that vivacious shop assistant and her teasing brown eyes and exploring hands. Sometimes I wonder too if... if... But no, no, no! I mustn't think of such things. Nevertheless, I can't help wondering if General de Gaulle ever did buy a plastic Mac in the holy city of Lourdes. And if he did, did it really look better on me than it did on him?

THE PAST REVISITED

Irish Independent, May 1986

Sometimes going back is a mistake – I know that now. After 54 years I returned last month to the German port of Wilhelmshaven, to the U-boat barracks that surrendered to a Royal Naval detachment in May 1945, the day the war ended in Europe. I went back expecting to relive the triumph and excitement of history being made as I had experienced it through the eager eyes of a young sailor. However, as an older and wiser man, what I saw and felt seemed strangely different.

Royal Naval Party 1735, attached to the Polish army, comprised 130 sailors dressed in uniforms of khaki and navy blue. Toting unfamiliar rifles and bayonets, we set out on the long trek through Belgium and Holland and eventually reached our objective, the German naval barracks in Wilhelmshaven. From here the searching U-boats had harried Atlantic convoys for five long years of war – but not any more.

After hours of bitter fighting the garrison surrendered and were given ten minutes to gather together what they could carry before being marched off to prison camp.

History doesn't tell of the looting done by members of victorious armies of the West, but they loot nonetheless. Apart from what the garrison had been forced to abandon, U-boat crews, still at sea, had left their personal belongings packed in their quarters. We looted the barracks; we kept what was valuable and we contemptuously destroyed what we didn't want.

Months afterwards, tired dispirited sailors, discharged from the German Navy, returned hopefully, walking and thumbing the long miles to Wilhelmshaven, anxious to gain possession of any pitiful bits of their property, the letters from loved ones, many now dead, the treasured photographs, the clothes, the jewellery, the personal belongings left behind for safety, and they were turned away from the gates. Victory was total and surrender was unconditional.

In the Mess that night in May '45 we drank many a toast to our great victory. A Polish officer, a university lecturer in Warsaw before the war, made a stirring speech in which he thanked us for the part we played in the liberation of his country.

"Thank you, my brave friends," he toasted, "you have liberated my beautiful Poland. Today we have finally weeded out everything that was evil in Europe and now its people can live for ever as free men and women." We cheered and refilled our glasses. "Long live Peace!" we toasted. "Long live peace in Europe!"

I thought of that Polish officer again last month when I stood there alone in the empty Mess. Since that great night long ago, allies have become enemies and enemies have become allies and I wondered if, wherever he was, he'd been happy to watch his beautiful Poland being handed over to a merciless Russian regime when the victorious Allies carved up the spoils of war. Was that what we fought for?

And as I walked the empty roads that once throbbed with the flush of marching boots, all now eerily silent, small doubts troubled my mind. These gaunt deserted buildings, had they really been a highly important military objective? But of course they were, I reassured myself, they must have been. I had helped bury three of my mates: Jock and Bob and Peter, as well as seven other comrades, in shallow graves beside the long road that stretched from Antwerp to Wilhelmshaven. Had they all died for nothing? We had marched hard and fought hard and died hard to get there in 1945. And hadn't we weeded out everything that was evil in Europe? So of course it was all worthwhile! But as I looked around the empty barracks, I felt somehow... cheated... unsure. Where was the peace in Europe that we bought with blood and toasted with champagne? In Bosnia? Kosova? Cechnya? Or even Northern Ireland? And suddenly I was no longer sure – not really sure. However, there is one thing I now know for certain! Going back was a mistake. Sometimes the past is best left in the past.

SAMMY

Ireland's Own, July 1951

Sammy was a pickpocket – a small-time pickpocket. The Gardai knew him as 'Sammy the Dip' and he was rather proud of that. But physically, mentally, morally, psychologically, pick any attribute you fancy, and you could be certain that Sammy was small in that area too. He was much too small of course, to handle the problem facing him one cold winter's morning after vindictive fate played a dirty trick on him the night before. (That, in itself, was quite a change – it was usually Sammy who played the dirty tricks.) Anyhow, that's why Sammy was crying.

His small, shifty eyes popped in horror when he read the story in the morning newspaper: 'an old lady had been found murdered and her life's savings', so the story said, had been stolen.

Now, Sammy was too small, morally, to be a murderer. He couldn't kill anything, not even a kitten, for God's sake! He could tie a can to its tail and laugh at the stupid animal's frantic efforts to escape from the maddening torture that the clanging can became. He had often played that trick when he was a kid, but murder? No way!

He read the story through again. Mrs Johnson (seventy-four) had been found gagged and bound in her own sitting room. She was dead some 12 hours when an alarmed neighbour called in the Gardai. Sammy's hand shook so much he could hardly read the account of his grim night's work. Her life savings: a measly 15 quid, in single coins, and for that he would have every bleedin' copper in the country looking for him. But, God, he hadn't killed her. There must be some mistake. He put the paper down and wiped his sweaty palms on the seat of his pants.

He had overheard two young soldiers discussing the old lady in a pub. They'd been invited to her house for tea. She was like that, apparently – her husband, a full-time soldier, had been killed in the war, and ever since, she, a lonely old woman, had been inviting lonely soldiers to her lonely old house to have a cup of tea and a bun to help pass her loneliness away. One of the soldiers reckoned that Mrs Johnson was supposed to be worth quite a few bob. That was enough for Sammy. He followed the two soldiers and noted the address. The rest was easy. Well, more or less . . . At ten o'clock, he knocked on her door. When she opened it unsuspectingly, a short, sharp clip to the chin put her out cold. Sammy tied her arms and legs with the cord of her dressing gown and knotted her scarf around her mouth to keep her quiet while he ransacked the house. Fifteen pounds had been his reward. Fifteen miserable bleedin' quid! And for that he was a murderer. The scarf must have been too tight or else she'd had a cold in the head or something and she wasn't able to breath properly. Suffocated! And he was a murderer. Sammy started to cry again. A shiver rippled through his heaving body. Sammy wasn't big enough to be a murderer. Sammy was small – like the kittens he used to torture with the cans tied on their tails . . .

He focused his eyes on the paper again and tried to think his way out of the problem. He wasn't used to this. Further down the column he saw, in bold print, the two words 'A Clue!' A cold, sinking feeling made his empty stomach heave. Good God! Already!

"This case shouldn't give us too much trouble," a

detective told our reporter. "We expect to make an early arrest." He declined further comment but our reporter understands that an 'unusual type' of button had been found at the scene of the crime . . .

Sammy's eyes ran down the front of his sports jacket. The three 'unusual' leather buttons stared back at him comfortingly. He heaved a sigh of relief. That had been a bad moment there! Yes, very bad, indeed. His sleeve caught on the chipped cup and knocked it off the table. He jumped and cursed at the same time – those effing buttons were always catching on something or other . . .

Something gripped his insides and squeezed. Buttons on his sleeves! He ran his fingers over them – three on the right sleeve and three on the left . . . One, two . . . he tried again . . . one, two! There was even a piece of the bloody cloth gone with the button. He flopped into the chair, his head on his hands. One, two, one, two, beat through his brain like the heavy ticking of an alarm clock. Two. Only two . . .

Sammy was too small for this. No, he really wasn't big enough to handle something like murder. A tear gathered in the corner of his eye and hung for a moment before tracing a white streak down his cheek. He was big for the first time in his life. The world wanted him; they were looking for him – all because of a miserable, missing button. And 15 lousy quid . . .

It was five long, lonesome minutes before he moved, before he started to think again. He had no overcoat. He had no other clothes. But he did have 15 quid. If he slipped out now and bought himself another jacket and burnt the old one, then who'd know? No, hang on a minute! Not a new jacket. That would only attract attention. What he needed was a second-hand jacket. His confidence grew as he thought it through. The idea about the second-hand jacket was good thinking. A clear head was all he needed... no panic, all coppers were fools. Sammy was no fool. He was Sammy the Dip. He was Sammy . . . the murderer.

Mounting panic flooded him but he fought it down. Another tear rolled over and some of his new-found confidence floated away on it.

He made up his mind suddenly. Burying his left hand, with the missing button, deep in his pocket, he went out. They sold second-hand clothing in Cronin's shop. He'd fool 'em yet. He wasn't so small . . .

Cronin's shop was just around the corner. The street was deserted. Cold rain beat on Sammy's face and washed some of the fear out of his system. Laid back was the attitude. Everyone wore second-hand clothes nowadays.

Mr Cronin himself was behind the counter. He eyed Sammy impersonally. "Good morning," he grunted. People never called Sammy "Sir". Unless they said it like in "Down, sir" as if they were talking to a dog. Mr Cronin's eyes were big and curious behind the thick glasses. Very big and very curious. Too curious, Sammy thought, suddenly afraid again.

Then he saw the newspaper opened at The Page. A small muscle started to twitch in his cheek. God in heaven, why had he been such a fool? Wasn't this just what the coppers expected him to do: buy a new jacket, a second-hand jacket. They'd probably been around to Cronin already to warn him to be on the lookout for a man buying a second-hand jacket, and he'd nearly walked into it. The net was closing around him. Slowly but surely. Every nerve in his body was taut. Cronin was staring at him, silently and patiently. Waiting, just waiting.

Sammy's eyes riveted on to a gaudy tie. £1.50 the price tag said. He'd fool 'em yet . . .

"A tie . . . " he started. He stopped and tried to clear his dry throat noisily. "I want a tie – that tie." He pulled two pound coins from his pocket and put them on the counter. Mr Cronin leaned back and took the tie off the rack and handed it to Sammy. He took the two coins. "I'll get you your change," he said and walked back to the office. Sammy watched him suspiciously. Had he noticed the missing button? Was he going to ring the cops?

At the door of the office, Mr Cronin stopped and turned around. His eyes met Sammy's. He smiled. It was a cold, humourless smile. He beckoned to someone in the office. A young girl came out and stood watching Sammy. Cronin went in. The girl just stood and watched.

Cold sweat broke out on Sammy's forehead. Eff her, why was she watching him like that? And why was Cronin taking so long to get the change? Was everybody always going to watch him like this? For 15 miserable quid . . . 13 now.

Sammy couldn't stand it any longer. He swung on his heel and hurried out the door. The girl opened her mouth but she didn't say anything. Sammy stuffed the tie into his trousers pocket. He wanted to run but that would only draw attention to himself. He pushed his head down into the rain and hurried to get back to the safety of his bed-sitter. He was empty. He was only Sammy – poor, small Sammy . . . a murderer.

"Hey, there, hang on!" Sammy looked back and saw the copper hurrying after him. He saw him out of the corner of his eye and he started to run then. To run away. Anywhere. He could hear the heavy steps pounding after him, the shouted order to stop. His breath whistled and laboured. He tripped and fell. The wind was knocked out of him. Fifteen miserable quid for this. He started to cry. He hadn't meant to kill the owld wan. He wouldn't kill anything – not even a kitten . . .

"I didn't mean it," he whimpered when the Guard jerked him to his feet. "I didn't mean to kill her – the gag, it must have slipped or something . . . "

Sammy blurted out the whole story to the Guard. He just listened and said nothing. The handcuffs snapped. Sammy didn't cry anymore. The young girl picked up the tie that had slipped out of Sammy's pocket outside the shop. The Guard had seen it too but Sammy started to run when the Guard called out to him to tell him that he'd lost his tie. She gave the tie to Mr Cronin. He smiled and wiped it clean and put it back on the rack.

Detective Sergeant Rogers was sitting at his desk with the telephone clamped between his shoulder and his ear. The Guard brought in Sammy. There was a buzz and a squeaky voice came over the line. Rogers smiled steadily at Sammy. He spoke into the mouthpiece: "O'Brien? Rogers. Forget that check-up at the army camp – we've got the buck-o who did it. It's Sammy the Dip. He told us all about it. What? Ah, no. That army uniform button we found had nothing to do with the case at all . . . "

THE DOLLEEN

Irish Monthly, July 1951

Ned tiptoed carefully down the narrow stairs past the half-open kitchen door, his daughter-in-law's nagging voice clawing around him like a shrill, whining drill. God bless us and save us, what a terrible life that woman gave his poor eejit of a son! Morning till night 'twas nothing but nag, nag, nag. How in the world she had ever produced such a lovely little girl as his granddaughter, Mary, he'd never know. Now there was sweetness itself, with the soft brown eyes and the lovely looks of his own dear wife, dead and gone these last 15 years.

His rheumy eyes sharpened as the voice from the kitchen droned on: "And what's he doing with the money he's getting from that nixer he's doing down the docks, answer me that, will you?" She answered the question herself. "Drinking it, you can be sure, drinking it and he eating us out of house and home as if the few pounds of his pension was quarter enough to compensate me for the loss of that lovely big room. I could get ten times as much from one of those Spanish students . . . "

Ned pushed back the catch on the door as quietly as possible and hobbled out before having to bear the indignity of hearing his own flesh and blood hum and haw half-heartedly before the all-powerful flood of feminine vituperation. She knew he'd been paid this morning for the night-watching job he was doing on the new dock by the river. And that poor amadán of a son he'd reared – not a word out of him in defence of his father, not a single bloody word.

Ned limped down the darkening street. His leg was at him again – he wouldn't be able to keep up the watching job much longer. Thanks be to God he'd soon be joining Mama in Heaven – she'd have a place kept for him. An owld fella like himself without the moth to look after him was a sad thing and he wouldn't be missed. God rest Mama's soul. His heart warmed again. Only little Mary, little Mary with her soft brown eyes and her loving kisses for Grandda, she'd miss him. She'd be four years old tomorrow. Four lovely blessed years, and she was growing more beautiful every day.

The man in the shop had the doll put aside for him. Ned handed over the £37. "It's for my little granddaughter," he told the man proudly. "She'll be four tomorrow and what a lovely little girleen she is – the spit of her grandmother . . . "

The man in the shop forced a smile as he tied the fancy string on the parcel. The world was full of old geezers who thought their granddaughters had the sun shining out of them. And a lot of them were a bit funny, like . . . Thank God 'twas nearly time to go home.

Ned took the parcel and made his way to the bus stop. It started to rain again. But it would be worth all this trouble tomorrow when he'd take the doll into Mary's room and see the happiness on the little mite's face. He'd be surely dead and gone before she was five. But she'd have this last nice present from Grandda and maybe when she'd get older and she'd look at the dolleen she'd think of her old Grandda and say a few prayers for his soul. And himself and Grandma would look down at her from Heaven and they'd ask God to bless her and watch over her and get her a good man who'd appreciate her.

On impulse, he turned into a newsagent's shop and

picked a birthday card. It had little angels flying around a huge cake with four candles on it and it said Happy Birthday to a Lovely Granddaughter. He borrowed a pen from the girl behind the counter and painfully wrote '*To darling Mary from Grandda.*' And then he added '*and Grandma.*'

She'd love the way the dolly closed its eyes when you put her flat down and then opened them again and said "Mama" when you lifted her up. And she'd love the card too. He was glad he thought of adding the bit about the card being from Grandma as well . . .

It was cold sitting in the watchman's hut by the river. The fire glowed in the brazier in front of him, but his aching old body needed more than a fire to keep the blood coursing through him. He opened the cardboard box and held the doll in front of him making sure that the heat of the fire didn't damage the crinkly dress or the flaxen hair. He put it flat on his lap and the doll's eyelashes fluttered shut. He stood it up straight on his knee and the eyes opened and it said "Mama".

Ned chuckled hoarsely. Sure now, wasn't that just the way the young fella used to be too, eh? When he held him on his knee long ago and told him stories about the war and things, wasn't he a fine boy with a fine future in front of him. And how they'd skimped and saved, Mama and himself, to put him to a good school with the Christian Brothers. And wasn't it always Mama he'd call for when he was in trouble. Just like the dolleen.

Ned put the doll back in the box. The life had gone out of him when Mama died. God rest her soul in Heaven. And when he'd close his eyes for the last time on this side and open them for the first time on God's side, Mama would be there to take his hand and show him where to go. He smiled. And when he'd meet her, he'd say "Mama!" Just like the dolleen.

His fingers found the rosary beads in the pocket of his overcoat and he mouthed a few quick Hail Marys. "Holy Mary, Mother of God, pray for my little granddaughter now and at the hour of her death, Amen. Hail Mary, full of grace . . . " His head nodded on his chest. The beads slipped from his tired fingers.

A distant clock struck four times. Ned sat up with a start. He rubbed his freezing hands together and poked at the dying fire. The dark river flowed silently down into the night. High above the fading lights of the city, a heavy cloud hung on the edge of a crescent moon. There was a sniff of rain on the wind. A dog barked and then it was eerily quiet again. Better do a round or two now. There wasn't much danger of anybody pinching anything around here but those jackeens who owned the place they'd blame him if anything was wrong in the morning.

Ned stretched himself stiffly and switched on the torch. Better take the dolleen with him – it wouldn't do to lose it now after all he'd been through to get it. He picked up the cardboard box and hobbled down the wharf flashing the torch to the right and left before him. The cold grasping waters lapped hungrily in the dark beneath him. Watch out now for those holes in the planks – the bad leg wouldn't stand up to any sudden twists. He flashed the torch at the darkness of an oil barrel. A big cat came spitting angrily from behind it and dashed between his legs. Ned jumped back, his heart jerking in fright. The box dropped from his hands.

"Shag ye," he whispered breathlessly. "Shag ye to Hell." His heart was thumping madly. His breath tore at his chest. He leaned on the barrel and tried to ease himself. The doll – the dolleen, oh my God, was it in the river? Then he saw it resting on the edge of the catamaran. He sighed his relief and stretching full length on the cold dark planks, he reached down. His fingers just touched the cardboard box. He stretched farther. His fingers grasped at it. A sudden stabbing pain flashed through his pumping chest. His breath caught in agony. A low moan trembled from his purple lips. "God have mercy on me, " he groaned.

The box slipped from him. It bounced on the catamaran and burst open. Another stabbing pain cut through his chest. Faintly above the lapping waters he heard "Mama" as his senses slipped from him. Darkness came over him. The doll's flaxen head bobbed and ducked in the swirling current of the river. "Mama" it called over and over again as the waves lifted it and dropped it again. And then it was sucked under into a long silence.

Ned opened his tired, heavy eyes. He could still hear the crying, "Mama! Mama!" He cocked his ear. But, no, that couldn't be the dolleen. He looked around him and knew immediately where he was – James's hospital. That's where Mama died, in a ward just like this one. There was a curtain around the bed. He closed his eyes again, trying to remember. The dolleen – oh, Jaysus, the dolleen. It was all coming back to him now – the dolleen in the river, the terrible pain in his chest.

"Mama! Mama!" He tried to sit up when he heard the voice. Could it be the dolleen – maybe it hadn't been lost after all . . . And then he heard his daughter-in-law:

"Shush Mary, darling, shush... I told him, nurse, I told him a hundred times he was too old to be working but would he listen? Oh no. And now all this trouble. And on my little daughter's birthday too . . . he's ruined it for the poor mite."

Ned closed his eyes. A stabbing pain ripped through his chest. The breath rattled out of him in a long tired sigh.

"Mama," he whispered hoarsely, "Mama!" His tired head rolled back, a slow smile fixed on his face. It was over at last – it was all over.

THE ROSE-RED CITY OF PETRA

Sunday Press, July 1985

Words, photographs, paintings, drawing, they can only reach out inadequately to the architectural wonders of Petra, for Petra will always remain as it has remained for over 2,000 years, a colourful enigma, a misty legend in the heart of Jordan's desert land. It is a city carved from the rose-red rock of Biblical times surviving into the present, but it is a city that must be experienced to be fully appreciated.

The Nabateans, an Arab tribe, created Petra during the second century before Christ. The Romans, under Emperor Trojan, conquered it in 106 AD and it flourished until the fourth century. And then, strangely and mysteriously, Petra became a misty fairy tale, an Atlantis-type legend whispered by fierce Bedouin tribesmen squatting around their desert campfires. And it stayed that way until 1812 when the Anglo-Swiss explorer, Johann Burckhardt, disguised as an Arab trader, rediscovered the lost city from the past.

Our visit to Petra was made on foot through the famous Siq – a mile-long gorge that zigzagged through the mountains that protected Petra for so many centuries. Never more than a few yards wide, the walls of the narrow gorge reach menacingly to a height of 400 ft., providing an impregnable entrance that defied invasion and discovery for over 2,000 years. The gorge is the result of a natural fault that seeped right through the mountain and under the awesome pressure of some prehistoric earthquake it simply split apart. Rock strata can still be seen to stop abruptly on one face of the chasm and pick up again immediately on the opposite face. The walls glow with bands of colour ranging from pearly white to gold to red, carmine and mauve. The sunlight, streaming from above, lights and picks out each new glorious colour and then, a few metres on, the walls close in and the dark and the shadow and the light fight together in a kaleidoscope of fiery colour. The visit to Petra would have been worthwhile just for the memorable trek through this canyon of beauty. But all that was but a poor foretaste of what was yet to come.

After a 20-minute spellbound walk, the Siq suddenly ended and we faced the most striking and memorable sight in a city that is a city of wonder: our first glimpse of the Khazne, the Treasury of Petra. By happy coincident we arrived there at exactly eleven o'clock and, as the sun strikes it fully at about that time, the Treasury was at its most brilliant and glowing pink-orange colour that explains why the city of Petra has been dubbed the rose-red city.

Seeming to be supported by six tall columns, the Treasury is, in fact, carved deeply into the solid rock of the mountain and even today the architectural detail is still wonderfully stark and fresh. The facade is approximately 92' wide and to the top of the urn, which surmounts the tent roof of the central kiosk, it measures 130'. The urn itself stands some 11' high. It is the urn that gives this building its name: Pharaoh's Treasury.

To the Bedouin who lived in desert tents, such giant buildings were undoubtedly the miraculous creations of the divine Pharaoh. According to their folklore the Pharaoh had deposited all his treasure in the huge urn and placed it forever out of human reach on the top of the monument. And, over the years, Bedouin warriors have expended much precious ammunition firing at the urn in an attempt to break it open. This practice has now been forbidden but the urn itself is riddled with bullet marks, legend having it that the lucky Bedouin who cracked it would be showered with gold and precious stones and riches beyond belief. The Wadi in which the Treasury stands is, understandably, known as the Wadi of the Urn.

From the Treasury the walk towards the centre of the city reveals a bewildering series of carved tombs and temples. A steep climb of up stairs and ramps and walkways brought us to the High Place of Sacrifice with its beautifully carved altar and wide drains to carry off the blood of the sacrificed victims.

Far below, the Roman Theatre, carved out of the hillside, at one time seated three to four thousand spectators in 33 rows of seats. Today it stands a rather bleak colourless monument to an Empire that once straddled the known world. A little farther on, the Cardo Maximus, the paved and colonnaded Roman Road marks the route that passed through the monumental public quarters of second-century Petra. Now it is in ruins, but this so-called Street of the Colonnades once knew a glory and a pride that matched even that of Rome itself.

Returning to the city centre, another series of beautiful monuments, all carved from the southern face of the rock, are known as the Royal Tombs. They include the Urn Tomb, a first-century monument that was converted into a Christian church in 446 AD and the Sextus Florentius Tomb that can be dated to about 130 AD, thanks to the Latin inscription still legible over the main doorway.

Petra is located just 165 miles southwest of the modern city of Jordan's Amman. Here the past and the present fuse in colourful history. Moses, wandering with the Israelites in the desert, struck water from a stone nearby. When John the Baptist was baptising in the Jordan River, Petra was a thriving centre of trade and commerce controlling the caravan routes between Egypt and Arabia. Today, Petra, so long lost to civilisation, has emerged again from the mists of timelessness to forge a new link between the present and the past. And because it is carved in solid rock, it will last forever.

COME INTO MY
SHOPPING PARLOUR . . .

The Irish Times, October 1980

It's out in the open, at last – modern shopping centres are scientifically designed not, as you might foolishly think, to satisfy the needs of the paying customers, but simply to separate them as quickly and as clinically as possible from their money.

A department of Britain's Reading University, The Centre for Advanced Land Use – CALUS for short, and I don't think they had any pun in mind – has carried out exhaustive studies in the science of conning shoppers into buying, not only what they don't want, but also a lot more of it. And because they have issued a special book for the guidance of planners and builders, we may now expect to be subjected more and more to the callous seductions of these psychological spiders who invite us into their shopping parlours.

If, for instance, you are one of those innocents who thinks it is mean and sneaky of supermarket owners to put a tray of sweets and chocolate bars at kiddy height just at the point where the unfortunate shopping mother, with her brood in tow, is queuing at the checkout, then you are due for a shock. That carry-on, literally, is kid's stuff. The modern conjob, according to recommendations made by CALUS, must start right at the drawing board in the architect's office when the shopping complex is being designed.

Up to now, you probably thought that those blasts of nice warm air that caress you when you enter modern shops, or closed-in shopping centres, are provided by considerate shop owners for your comfort. Though it may help to keep you warm, apparently it is part of a deliberate plan to create a psychological womb-effect. You feel nice and warm and safe inside the shopping mall, and it is cold and dangerous out there in that nasty old world. So you don't leave the store. You stay and shop till all your money is gone. (Even commercial womb-effects wear a bit thin, I'm afraid, when all your money is gone.)

Getting in and out of these complexes calls for special comment in CALUS's book. The architect is advised to design the centre with the lobsterpot in mind – easy to get into but as difficult as possible to get out.

"The best entrances," say the authors, "are those which attract shoppers into the centre, yet need a conscious effort to locate the exits, when the shopper wants to leave."

So that's why the sign marked 'Exit' is, without doubt, the smallest and least eye-catching sign in any shopping centre. And, even after you have located the sign, you will still be directed to take a few wrong turns before you escape to the safety of the car park.

If you happen to get tired as you search for the exit, you may of course sit down and rest on one of the seats so thoughtfully provided for you by the management.

'Thoughtfully' is the keyword here. Back again to the book: "If seats are too comfortable, shoppers will stay too long sitting down. A ten-minute seat would be ideal." So that's why the seats are so hopelessly uncomfortable; they are usually backless, hard and spine-destroying. But if you were allowed to sit reading your paper, relaxed and cosy in womb-effect comfort, then you would not be spending money and that, definitely, is not to be encouraged. Those seats are deliberately designed so that, after a maximum of ten minutes, the torture of shopping becomes more acceptable than the torture of resting.

Full-page ads in the daily papers extolled the virtues, comforts and glamour of shopping in the recently opened Irish Life Mall in the heart of Dublin. Says the blurb: "Based on the recommendations of international consultants" – CALUS, no doubt –"the Irish Life Mall achieves a concept in shopping never previously attained in Ireland."

They can say that again. Cut-stone walls, floors throughout finished in glazed brown clinker tiles, low dark ceilings with subdued lighting, blood-red panelling, temperature at a constant 70F, and, in contrast to this comforting womb-like dimness, the surrounding shops are brightly-lit welcoming centres that draw us cunningly like silly moths to the expensive flame.

And please don't miss the colourful beauty of the hanging gardens and the fountain and pool. Not another psychological catch surely? I'm afraid so. The happy gurgle of fountains, say the experts, help us to feel uninhibited and free. And what do we do when we are uninhibited and free? Indeed, yes. We spend our money freely and uninhibitedly.

If, at any stage, you feel like rushing out of one of these shopper-traps – if you can find the exit, that is – you then become a statistic under the heading of PFD – pedestrian flow density. The planners and psychologists had you fully in mind when they thought up the one about "visual stops."

What are visual stops? you ask. Visual stops may be either ten-minute seats, hobby horses and suchlike where the kids can squander the last of your small change, a gesture to the arts in the form of an ultramodern piece of sculpture, or even a potted plant. But The Book makes it quite clear that these must be placed strategically in the centre of the malls so that the flow of spending pedestrians – PFD – is forced to the sides and close to the inviting shop doors. You see? The suckers must never be given a clear run to the exit under any circumstances. If at all possible, make sure that they can't ever see the exit. Make them dawdle along slowly; that way they'll spend and spend and spend. And isn't that what it's all about?

So there it is. Your modern hyper-market, super-store, shopping complex, call it what you will, it is a scientifically designed trap to strip you naked of all you've got, your wit, your intelligence, your dignity, but above all, your hard-earned money. And it's no use fighting it. You're only a baby in the hands of the psychological manipulators, I'm afraid. It's that womb-effect thing, you see.

MY BRIEF BRUSH WITH THE WORLD OF ART

RTÉ, *Sunday Miscellany*, August 2002

For me it was just another appointment – 'Meet Mr Graves,' the diary said, 'three o'clock at his residence in Rathfarnham – he wants a job done on the avenue.'

That was over 50 years ago but it was only when I read his recent obituary that I learnt that the Mr Graves I met that afternoon was a very famous person.

I was a Rep with a macadam company and my job was to survey all proposed work, estimate the cost and do the hard sell. Boring stuff really, but occasionally, out of the blue, along came someone different – like Morris Graves.

Mr Graves was a gangling American in his fifties. It became evident that he was an artist when he showed me into his spacious drawing room. The walls hung with paintings, more were stacked on the table and there were even some leaning against the piano.

"Excuse the mess," he apologised, "I'm packing for an exhibition in New York." His eyebrows lifted. "You into art?" I wasn't, not one bit, but in our business the rules of the game were clear: humour the customer.

"Oh yeah!" I lied, "very much so." That seemed to please him.

"Good!" he said, "First the paintings and then we'll look at the avenue."

And though I didn't realise it then, art lovers the

world over would have given their eyeteeth, a leg, an arm and anything else they owned, to be in my shoes that afternoon. You see, what I didn't know until I read the obituary, was that Morris Graves, late of Oregon, USA was one of the world's greatest painters – right up there with the Dutch Masters, in fact – and he was inviting me to preview an exhibition of his paintings about to be staged in New York. And to be honest, I wasn't even vaguely interested.

As we viewed each painting Mr Graves held forth earnestly on Abstract Art and Cubism and stuff that meant absolutely nothing to me. And the paintings? Well, they were nice, I suppose – lots of Chinese vases and exotic flowers and birds – Mr Graves seemed particularly proud of one long-legged fellow pecking at a snail. But it was nothing that I could relate to. It was all a bit weird, really.

"Right then," he said, abruptly, just when I thought he'd never finish, "let's go look at the avenue." I think he'd guessed that I wasn't really into this art stuff. Mind you I did try, but you know how it is...

The avenue was in good condition – nothing that a coat of macadam wouldn't fix. But before I could launch into my sales spiel, Mr Graves started off about a road he had seen in Connemara, the likes of which he had never seen in all his life before. This road, he explained, was sculpted with irregularly-shaped indentations, each one brimming with water, and in the long rays of the setting sun the pools glittered like diamonds scattered on a dark carpet. I could hardly believe what I was hearing. And the snaking ribbon of bright green grass that grew down the centre of it – my God, you'd have to see it on an autumn evening to appreciate such colour, such beauty... a masterpiece! I stopped him there.

"Mr Graves," I said, "If you think roads like that can

be custom built, you're wrong." Maybe I sounded a trifle sarcastic. "Only time, negligence and sheer bloody laziness could create such a masterpiece..."

The obituary said that Morris Graves was at the very pinnacle of his illustrious career when he came to Ireland in search of an unspoilt landscape and environment in which his genius might flourish further. And it went on: "In Ireland, however, this gifted visionary did not find the virgin paradise he was looking for, so he moved on, never to return."

Oh dear! I do hope it wasn't anything I said...

THE FRENCH ARE IN THE BAY

Ireland's Own, April 1994

A visit to the French Armada Centre in Bantry, Co. Cork is an impressive cultural and historic experience by any standards. It is disappointing, however, to find that there is no mention or record of the tragic part played by a little dog named Pompey in the historic events of December 1796 when a formidable French fleet, inspired by the efforts of Wolfe Tone, sailed into Bantry Bay.

Gibson, in his History of Cork, had this to say about Wolfe Tone: "He did as much as any man could do to conquer Ireland by French bayonets, in order that it might be converted to French republican opinions, or to anything but what it was. He bore an undying hatred to the English rule. He would, he said 'prefer that France, Spain, the Autocrat of Russia, or the devil himself had the country rather than England.'"

On that fateful morning in 1796, James Sweeney, a Bantry man, was walking his dog on the hills overlooking the stormy seas when he saw the billowing sails of the first of more than 50 French men-of-war looming up out of the early morning mist. Hastily, he gathered up his dog, a small spaniel bitch named Pompey, and with her safely tucked under his cape, he hurried to Bantry to report the arrival of the French fleet.

According to Gibson the French fleet had on board,

"15,000 soldiers under the command of General Hoche, together with one thousand, one hundred stands of arms, 20 pieces of field artillery, nine large siege guns, mortars, howitzers, 61 thousand kegs of gun powder, seven million ball cartridges, seven hundred thousand flints and a motley supply of small arms."

Rebel West Cork waited with bated breath; their long-awaited liberation from the English yoke was at hand. The French, with a huge and heavily-armed invading force, were at last in the Bay.

Wolfe Tone, founder of the United Irishmen, was on board *The Indomitable*, a fighting ship of 80 guns. His diary entry for 22 December 1796 reads: "This morning at eight o'clock we have neared Bantry Bay considerably but the fleet is terribly scattered." And four days later, 26 December 1796, he wrote, "Last night, at half past six o'clock, with a heavy gale of wind still from the east, we were surprised by the admiral's frigate running under our quarter, and hailing *The Indomitable* with orders to cut our cable and put to sea instantly. The frigate then pursued her course, leaving us all in the utmost astonishment. All our hopes are now reduced to get back to the safety of Brest." And he added in deep despair: "Well, let me think no more about it. It is lost and let it go."

History does not fully record the reasons why, having successfully made the hazardous journey from Brittany, this mighty French army failed to land in Bantry. Whatever the reason, the fleet sailed away into the turbulent darkness of the night of 26 December 1796, and returned to France having remained off Bantry for just four days. Wolfe Tone's attempt to rid his country forever of the hated English invader had come to naught.

What history does record, however, is the sad fate of

James Sweeney's dog, Pompey. When Sweeney raised the alarm in Bantry he was immediately dispatched in panic-stricken haste to warn the authorities in Cork. Mr Sweeney, born and reared in Bandon was chosen for the task because he, better than most, knew all the shortcuts and byways through the wilds and forest of West Carbery at that time. In fact, he accomplished the daunting journey in half a day and a night, having used up three horses almost to the point of death. However, what Mr Sweeney didn't know was that in his haste to carry out his orders he had forgotten to lock up little Pompey, and the poor animal, in her loyal love had followed him unbeknownst, all the way from Bantry.

In Cork, having passed-on the information to the authorities about the imminent invasion by the French, Mr Sweeney returned to the stable where he had left his horse. A Bandon historian of the time, George Bennet, wrote of the incident:

"To his utter amazement and dismay, he found his little pet lying on the saddle-cloth in the stable, prostrate and gasping for breath. Upon seeing him, little Pompey made an attempt to get up and greet her old master as usual, but the effort was too much for her; she fell back and after a few feeble struggles she was dead.

"Deeply saddened, Mr Sweeney carefully wrapped Pompey's body in the cloth on which she lay; and, on his way back to Bantry, he had his family grave in Bandon opened, and with his own hands he laid the remains of his faithful little companion amongst the dust and ashes of his kindred."

COME, DANCE WITH
SALOME IN ISRAEL!

Irish Independent, November 1978

Tourism has hit the number one spot in Israel's economic build-up pushing citrus fruits into second place with the glittering diamond industry running a close third. But today's tourism has its emphasis veering in a different direction. The pilgrims, following in the footsteps of the Master, still make up the vast bulk of the huge influx of visitors arriving daily at the airport in Tel Aviv. The Holy Places still beckon to Christians all over the world. The peace of the Shepherds' Field outside Bethlehem may be disturbed by the distant sound of gun-fire from a nearby army practice range but the calmness of the Church of the Nativity, the Garden of Gethsemane and the Church of the Holy Sepulchre still reaches back over two thousand years and fills the pilgrim's heart with that promised peace that surpasses all understanding.

Within the walls of the City of Jerusalem nothing seems to have changed in thousands of years. Along the Via Dolorosa Arab traders still pluck your sleeve, inviting you into stalls to haggle over a bewildering array of goods, from leatherwork to silver craftsmanship.

The ancient past lives here and the monotonous Moslem call to prayer still rings out across the squalid rooftops as it did when the Crusaders stormed across these very hills. The plodding camel and the patient ass are as much part of today's scene as they were in the time of Christ. Nothing has changed. The Palestine of the Master is still with us.

But less than five minutes walk away, outside the old city walls, the tourist returns to an hotel that offers a combination of modern comfort and first-class cuisine, air-conditioned rooms, friendly, cheerful bars, bedrooms with a private bath, televisions and balconies that overlook the Old City with its teeming poverty and its glorious memories of a never-to-be forgotten past.

Tel Aviv, for its part, has no pretensions to being associated in any way with the ancient past. Here the present has overtaken the past and made it its own. Ancient Jaffa, the gateway to Jerusalem since Biblical times, is one of Palestine's oldest cities and in 1906, when conditions for Jewish settlers became too overcrowded, a group of pioneers left Jaffa and started a garden suburb at nearby Ahurzat Bavit.

Gradually more and more settlers were drawn there and a new city, Tel Aviv, became the social and cultural centre as well as the unofficial capital during the years when Israel was an embryo state.

Today on the Sunshine Coast, Tel Aviv is a city of the seventies. Day and night there is action everywhere to keep the tourist and the curious happily on the move. Twelve miles of glorious beach, under the blazing Mediterranean sun, sweep within a stones throw from the city centre. Bustling modern shops contrast starkly with the biblical-type activity of the marketplace in Old Jaffa, referred to almost contemptuously in tourist literature as the Flea Market.

At night the city lights up in a flickering array of neon signs sweeping aside the tropical dark, and whatever your idea of entertainment, Tel Aviv offers it on a plate – the pop scene with its swinging discos throbs and pulsates and beats out a rhythm that the tropical stillness and mystery make heavy with romance. Nightclubs and concert halls abound and ballet is now a big thing, especially since the arrival in 1974 of world famed dancers Valery Panov and his wife Galya, fleeing persecution in Russia. Tel Aviv is a city of hustle and bustle and it vibrates to the tempo of the new Land of Israel.

Happily for its very energetic tourist board, Israel is one of those rare countries that offers the visitors a wide variety of geographical settings and cultural variations in a relatively small area. In just a few hours the traveller can go from the lush, green Galilee region to the stark, bare desert wilderness, or leave the bustling Tel Aviv metropolis and reach the quiet calm of the Dead Sea.

The bewildering geographical changes are unbelievable. The Valley of Jezreel, a vast triangular valley of bountiful fertility, stretches between the mountains of Galilee in the north and the mountains of Samaria in the south. And a few short hours away the stark, intimidating Judean desert, with its goat-flocks and shepherds, merges into the Dead Sea and the Sinai desert, still littered with the debris of war and destruction.

The desert stretches from the hills of Judea to the Red Sea but, today, good new roads and modern accommodation and means of transport and a tireless Tourist Board, have opened it up as an exciting world of unusual vegetation and wild life, a place of rugged beauty and nature in the exposed raw.

The Dead Sea, the lowest point on earth, 1,300 feet below sea-level, has a concentration of minerals so high that the swimmer may float on his back and read a book.

Further south, on the shores of the Red Sea. The ancient city of Eilat, once the port of King Solomon, is being developed as a resort so delightful that it attracts visitors all the year round. According to statistics, it may rain at most once a month from November to March, and never in the other months.

The Red Sea teems with tropical fish that flash and dazzle in the crystal clear waters and skin-divers and scuba-divers the world over, look to Eilat as their place of pilgrimage. At night the city's hotels and nightclubs burst into a swinging, modern life of their own. Forgotten for the moment is the ancient port of Solomon and the vast hinterland of sprawling desert that bakes and shimmers in the ever-blazing sun. A few years ago a nightclub was opened in Eilat called the End of the World. It might, more appropriately, have been called the Beginning of the World – a brave, new world that has opened up the desert where once the passing Bedouin pitched his lonely tent.

Sodom and Gomorrah, the nearby ancient cities of the desert, are not remembered in thriving Eilat. The new city of the desert is going its own way and it looks for its prosperity and guidance to the future, not the past. It is an integral part of the new Israel.

Modern Palestine is a country of contrasts and a contrast of cultures, a contrast of times, a contrast of high hopes. Torn by wars for 3,000 years, destroyed, rebuilt, devastated and recreated, it still feverishly seeks its identity. It is old but it is young; it is a holy land, but it is a swinging land. Above all, however, it is a land fast catching up with a world that, 2,000 years ago, it led out of the past. The wandering Jew is home at last, and the travelling Gentile is a very welcome guest.

MATCH OF THE DAY

Woman's Way, October 1991

Maria stood uncertainly inside the door of the cafe, struggling with her dripping umbrella. Among the crowd of diners, all of whom seemed to be staring intently at her, there were at least three men who had well-trimmed beards and, as far as she could tell, they were all tall.

"I am six feet two, and I have a beard – well-trimmed mind you . . . " That's what the man who rang her had said after the computer dating agency had arranged for them to meet. Maria had liked the cheery note in his voice. "I'll be waiting outside the Café Clare, but if it's raining I'll get a table inside and keep an eye out for you."

Just then, to add to her misery, Maria's spectacles started to steam up from the heat of the café. Oh, my goodness, she though to herself, how did I ever allow myself to get involved in this sort of thing?

Panicking, she reached into her bag to get a tissue. That was when the umbrella opened again. It had been acting up for over a week now. Either get rid of it or get it fixed, Mam had said. She struggled with the catch, at the same time trying to open the café door so that she could escape out of this place. "You must be Maria Nolan." The voice came from way above her, but now her spectacles were completely steamed over. "I'm Michael D'Arcy," he said.

Maria nodded miserably. With her free hand she whipped off the now useless spectacles. The umbrella was taken from her and she heard it snapping shut. Suddenly the large, dark form took shape, slightly out of focus but clear enough to show the dark blue of the eyes, the slightest ripple of grey touching the temples, the even teeth. And yes, the beard was neatly trimmed.

"I'm – I'm really sorry," Marie said, flopping gratefully into the seat in the alcove. He cut her short. "Please don't even think about it, it could happen to a bishop – or even a Reverend Mother!"

Maria polished her glasses and replaced them. Her grey eyes met his and she was surprised to see a sudden deep flush spread above his beard and into his forehead and ears.

"My turn for blushes," he grinned ruefully. Maria tried to remember the opening remarks she had practiced again and again behind her librarian's desk at the Town Hall. "I've never done this sort of thing before . . . " She stopped abruptly, realising that it was not what she wanted to say at all.

Just then the umbrella, which he was still holding under the table, made a snapping sound and tried to open. He smothered it with large brown hands and then looked down in dismay at the twisted ribs.

"Oh my God, I'm afraid I've damaged it. I never realised that umbrellas were such delicate things." Stress and a strange excitement welled up inside Maria, threatening to explode.

Oh, please, please, she told herself, don't giggle. Then she giggled. He look at her in relief, his eyes taking in the auburn hair touching her shoulders, the grey eyes under the large fashionable glasses and the rather wide mouth that always seemed to be just on the verge of a smile.

He reached across the table and took her hand in his. "Let's start this again from the beginning and see if we can make a better go of it," he grinned, "You Maria, me Michael..."

* * * *

Maria's mother would have none of it. "Are you telling me you went out with a man, a complete stranger that some stupid computer picked out for you? Good God, what would your father have thought?"

Maria smiled to herself. Ever since Dad had died, she had become the centre of Mam's life. Every morning she packed her off to work with a flask and a packet of sandwiches, and every evening she had a good hot dinner waiting for her when she got home. Mam picked up the umbrella.

"Did you get this fixed?" she asked. Then she saw the badly-crushed ribs. Maria shook her head ruefully. "Put it in the bin, Mam," she told her. "Michael broke it." She saw the look of amazement on her mother's face. "He didn't mean to – it just started opening under the table in the café and he, well, he sort of crushed it." Her voice trailed off in a slight giggle then as she remembered the shocked look on Michael's face. The look on her mother's face was even more shocked. "He, he's a very big man," she offered by way of an explanation.

"Does the computer know that he goes around crushing umbrellas?" her mother demanded, eyeing the now useless umbrella. "It's a good thing you didn't meet him down some dark lane. God only knows what he'd have done. You're not meeting him again, I hope."

Maria nodded. "Of course I'm meeting him again, Mam. And he's not at all the savage brute you're making him out to be." She coloured slightly. "In fact, he's a very gentle sort of person. He plays rugby – in the scrum or something . . . "her voice trailed off as her mother's uneasy eyes watched her curiously. "I don't – I don't know too much about rugby."

Her mother examined the crushed umbrella and sighed. Maria was right – it was fit for the bin. "You don't know too much about men either, I'm afraid," she answered shortly, "if you're going to allow some stupid computer to pick one for you. I do hope you're not going to bring this person round here to the house. God only knows what he'd do to my furniture."

Maria could feel her mother's protective certainty reaching out to take charge of her. "Please, Mam, don't worry! I know you still think I'm, only a baby and need to be protected from the world, but I assure you I know what I'm doing and, anyway, he's coming here tomorrow evening – we're going to the pictures. You'll meet him then and you'll see I'm right."

And she added defensively, "Mam, he's really nice, even if a computer did find him for me. And he's a lot nicer than anybody I ever found for myself."

* * * *

The next evening as Maria put the finishing touches to her face she could still sense her mother's disapproval. "I'll be out in the garden," she called from the kitchen. "I don't know how I'll ever get it into shape."

Since Dad had died, the garden, his pride and joy, had deteriorated into a spreading wilderness of grass and weeds, but Maria knew her Mam was going out there just to avoid meeting Michael. She smiled tightly to herself, her own steely determination showing. You're going to meet him whether you like it or not, she promised herself. I'll see to that.

"Come out and meet my mother," she said to Michael when he arrived to pick her up in a rather battered yellow Volkswagen. "She's trying to get the garden into shape."

She smiled when she caught the frosty glare from her mother's eyes. Mam looked so frail standing there among the foot-high weeds with a heavy garden fork in her hands, but her quick glance took in the tall bearded man whose hobby seemed to be crushing umbrellas. Computer dating, indeed! She had never heard of the like – though, mind you, he was good-looking and the shy blush on his face was quite becoming.

She was suddenly aware of the fact that she was wearing a rolled-down pair of her late husband's old Wellingtons. Maria grinned wickedly, noting her mother's quick embarrassment. "How do you do?" she said politely. "You'll have to excuse my gardening gear."

Michael took the extended hand, which seemed to get lost in his huge grip. "Pleased to meet you, Mrs Nolan," he said. "Maria didn't tell me you were into gardening." His eyes were slightly puzzled as he surveyed the wilderness stretching back to the high garden wall.

Maria noticed his bewilderment. "I'm afraid we're not really as keen as Dad was," she faltered. "Anyway, we'd better hurry if we're going to catch the first house." She smiled at her mother. "I'll see you later, Mam, and please don't worry."

Michael hesitated at the side gate and looked again at the garden. "Look, Mrs Nolan," he blurted, "we don't have a match on Saturday – I don't know if Maria told you that I play rugby with the local team – but if you like, I wouldn't mind coming round and giving you a hand with the digging. I quite enjoy gardening, but now that I'm living in a flat . . . I used to do it all at home." His boyish smile was eager. "I could be here at about one o'clock on Saturday if that's okay with you?"

At exactly one o'clock on Saturday, Maria heard the doorbell ring. "I'll get it, Mam," she called. "Its probably Michael."

Maria gasped in astonishment when she saw the burly figure in boots, black stockings, white shorts and a yellow and blue jersey standing on the doorstep. Michael's bearded face was blushing in embarrassment. "It's a long story," he started. Behind him a line of similarly attired men were streaming from a bus parked outside the gate, each carrying a gardening implement. A small man in a bowler hat and overcoat followed the team, all the while supervising the transport of a heavy rotovator.

"Right then, Michael!" the man in the bowler hat called, "where's the action? We haven't all day. Let's get stuck in, lads."

"What on earth . . . " Maria heard her mother's voice behind her. "The computer has gone mad – they must have pushed the wrong button and now you've got a bunch of rugby-playing clones."

Michael found his voice at last. "It's all right, Maria, Mrs Nolan," he reassured them. "It's just that I got my dates wrong and we do have a match today after all. When I told the trainer I couldn't play because I'd promised you to come and help with the digging, well, all the lads insisted on coming. The groundsman has supplied us with equipment, so it won't take us long to dig over your garden."

Mr McCarthy, the groundsman, sat with Maria and Mrs Nolan on the garden seat under the sycamore tree and supervised the operation. "Won't take more than half an hour to get through this lot," he said filling his pipe, "not with a well-trained bunch of lads like these. We'll get all the weeds and stuff down into the corner and you can compost it, if that's okay with you, Mrs Nolan?" He glanced at his watch. "We have plenty of time yet – we don't have to be on the field until half-three. Ever watch rugby?"

Maria and her mum shook their heads, speechless. "We're a new club," he went on, "but we'll be really on our feet by the end of the season – then we'll be able to provide better facilities for supporters. You should come along – we need all the help and support we can get."

* * * *

Four months later, after planting out a new row of lettuce seeds, Maria's mum sat back on her seat under the sycamore and looked proudly down the garden bathed in the warm spring sunshine. Row after row of cabbages, beans, peas and lettuces peeped up in tidy lines from the dark soil stretching back to the garden wall with its high bank of flaming daffodils and tulips. Dad would be so proud of this display, she thought, a small pain touching her heart.

Mrs Murphy, Mrs Nolan's neighbour, looked over the fence. "Between the daffs and the tulips and the football jerseys you have a beautiful show of colour there," she called, pointing to the billowing clothesline bending under the weight of 17 yellow and blue jerseys swinging in the breeze.

"We're in the League Final on Saturday," Maria's mum said proudly "and that's it, I'm afraid, for this season." She shook her head. "Goodness me, but I'll miss my weekly outings to the matches and just when I was getting the hang of it – the scrums and things." She heard the whistle of the kettle coming to the boil in the kitchen. "But what with Maria's wedding next month and Michael coming to live here with us, well, I'm sure I'll understand it all perfectly before the new season starts." She grinned mischievously and added under her breath, "but computer dating, now that's something I'll never understand – even if it does work."

When a Yo-Yo Divided the Orange and the Green

RTÉ, *Sunday Miscellany*, May 1994

When my grandson, an English boy aged twelve, asked me what caused the troubles between Protestants and Catholics in Northern Ireland, my mind fled back over 60-odd years to a yo-yo contest in the Cox Memorial Hall in the town of Dunmanway, West Cork – just about as far from the North as you can get.

The Protestant community erected Cox's Hall in memory of Sir Richard Cox, Lord High Chancellor of Ireland, Speaker of the House of Lords and founder in 1641, of the garrison town of Dunmanway. Writing about the census of 1751, Sir Richard's grandson, the second Baronet, said proudly; "Blessed by God, here in Dunmanway, there is a decline in the papist population who in 1749 were 402, and are now down to 389. The Protestants are now 410 strong – an increase of 5."

By Christmas of 1930, when the yo-yo contest took place at a sale of work in Cox's Hall, the figures, which had so delighted Sir Richard, had changed significantly. Though we were still a mixed community, the Catholic numbers had increased and the Protestants were now in the minority. And as well as worshipping in different churches, we also, unfortunately, had separate cultural and recreational facilities provided for us by those same church authorities. We were forbidden to pray together and we were not encouraged to play together. And the only reason that a Catholic would support a Protestant sale of work in Cox's Hall during the 1930 Christmas feast of Peace and Goodwill was a simple economic one – there were bargains to be picked up.

The rules of the contest were simple. On the umpire's signal, all contestants played their yo-yos and the contestant who survived longest won the prize – three large apples. Twenty boys, ranging in age from about 7 to 14, took the stage, the signal was given and battle commenced.

Up and down, up and down went 20 yo-yos of every colour and size, screwed up faces holding concentration to its peak, no interference allowed, every man for himself and may the best yo-yo win. The minutes passed and the crowded hall had now gathered around the stage. Shouts of encouragement called on Patrick or George to "take it aisy, boy," or "steady it up, old chap." One by one, contestants fell out and left the stage. A deathly silence had fallen on Cox's Hall. The numbers on stage grew less and less and I suddenly realised that there were only two of us still competing. The moment of truth was at hand.

Out of the corner of my eye, I could see my opponent, a boy of about my own age. Unlike me in an Aran gansey knitted by my mother, short pants, knee-length stockings and good strong boots, he wore a blazer, long pants and a collar and tie. I recognised him as the son of the Protestant bank manager, home from boarding school for Christmas. My yo-yo was made of timber, about two inches in diameter, painted red and, no doubt, one of millions churned out by some factory in Birmingham. I had paid tuppence for it in Barry's shop in Castle Street. His yo-

yo, by contrast, was at least six inches in diameter, made of tin and painted, of all colours, a vivid green. Two cleverly placed holes made it whistle as it went up and down. It was definitely not out of Barry's shop – it was, at least, Selfridges, if not Harrods. But I wasn't worried. I knew my yo-yo. I could keep it going up and down till the cows came home, or longer if need be.

At this stage you could cut the tense air in the hall. The crowd was silent, divided into two groups by the invisible wall of hundreds of years of troubled history. Every eye followed the two yo-yos, up and down, up and down, mine doing a steady swish, swish, his going tweet, tweet, warbling up, warbling down, and my heart jumped when I noticed something – his yo-yo was wobbling slightly while mine was steady as a rock. I had his measure. Then came disaster.

Maybe my yo-yo was suffering from fatigue for suddenly, without wobble or warning, it disintegrated – one red half bounced across the stage and I was left holding a string with the other half hanging in limp defeat. I couldn't believe it – the Protestant's yo-yo was still whistling up and down like an Orangeman's flute on the 12th of July.

I hurried off the stage, trying desperately to hold back the hot tears. Applause broke out for the victor but I knew deep down that the hands that clapped him were Protestant hands, just as I knew that the hands that patted my head in sympathy were Catholic hands. I had lost the yo-yo contest and in my seven-year-old heart, I felt that I had failed the Catholic community of Dunmanway and, of course, His Holiness, Pope Pius XII in Rome.

That's why I thought back to the yo-yo contest of 60-odd years ago when my grandson asked me how the Northern Ireland troubles had started. I tried to explain that religious and historical differences had erected an artificial barrier between neighbours, and evil men on both sides had exploited the situation for their own ends. Inevitably, the poison spread till even innocent children, playing with their toys, became entangled in a poisonous web of hatred and distrust. My grandson heard me out in silence and nodded his polite thanks. Being English though, I don't think he understood anything of what I told him.

THE LADY IN WHITE

RTÉ, *Sunday Miscellany*, December 2002

When the autumn evenings close over Kinsale's harbour the shadowy walls of Charles Fort stand high against the long skyline. Then, say the local fishermen, the ghostly figure of the Lady in White may be seen on the ramparts searching, ever searching for the lost love of her life.

According to historian Smith writing in 1850, the construction of Charles Fort, named in honour of King Charles the Second, was started in 1670. "This fort," Smith says "is so situated that all ships coming into harbour must sail within a pistol shot of the royal battery. It stands one mile east of Kinsale, and hath a regiment of foot always quartered in it."

Colonel Warrender was governor of the fort in 1750. A strict disciplinarian, he handed down the death sentence for even minor breaches of discipline. His only daughter, whom he adored, had the rather unusual name of Wilful and she had just married Sir Trevor Ashurst. According to Smith, the happy couple were walking along the battlements on the evening of their wedding when Wilful saw some wild flowers growing on the rocks below.

"Oh, Trevor," she said, "how lovely they are and how I wish I could get some of them." But before Sir Trevor could reply, a sentry, on duty beside them volunteered: "If you wish, Sir, I shall climb down and get the flowers for your lady, but you will have to act as sentry while I am away."

The sentry's offer was accepted and he hurried away

in search of a rope while Sir Trevor donned his long cape and shouldered the musket. Wilful, finding the evening air a little chilly returned to their room. The rocks below the battlements were sharp and slippery and the soldier found the task wasn't as easy as he first thought. Sir Trevor, his brain dulled, no doubt by the liberal drafts of wine he had consumed at the wedding feast, dropped off to sleep. Unfortunately, just then, Governor Warrender did his night rounds.

When he came to the sitting sentry he challenged him. There was no reply. The Governor barked again. But there was only the murmur of the restless waves on the rocks below. Without hesitation, Governor Warrender drew his pistol and shot the sleeping sentry through the heart. Brusquely, he ordered the body to be carried inside and only then was the enormity of the tragedy discovered. Worse was to follow. Wilful, still in her wedding gown, returned to join her husband and when she saw his dead body, she screamed, and before she could be restrained, she threw herself over the battlements on to the rocks below.

Her father, the Governor, overcome with grief, retired to his quarters and shot himself through the head. In a matter of minutes a bunch of wild flowers growing on the rocks below Charles Fort had brought about a triple family tragedy.

Down the years, according to the local fishermen, the tragic figure of the Lady in White may still be seen wandering distraught amongst the ruins of the fort, searching, searching, forever searching. And, as if mocking the poor tortured spirit, the wild flowers that brought such tragedy into her young life still bloom and blossom on the rocks below.

Shaun Nash – The Hanging Judge

RTÉ, *Sunday Miscellany*, June 1990

West Cork history records the name of a seventeenth-century judge whose propensity for handing down the death sentence made him feared by guilty and innocent alike. Shaun Nash, renowned as a bloodthirsty Captain of the Bandon Militia, and referred to by his peers on the bench as "a rather uncouth fellow", was appointed Provost of Bandon in 1691.

Describing this period, a local historian, George Bennett, records that: "so infested was this neighbourhood with deserters from Sarsfield's divisions, and desperadoes let loose upon society by the surrender of Limerick, that those living in the country parts could not count on being alive in 24 hours."

To grapple with this situation Provost Nash armed himself with extraordinary powers and in a very short time his name was feared and reviled throughout West Cork.

Known variously as Jack the Devil, Ould Jack, Shaun Dearg or Jack the Hanger, it must be said in fairness that when first appointed, Nash tried to be scrupulously fair in the administration of law and order. However, the endless flow of outlaws and rapparees brought before him for trial soon began to affect both his patience and his judgement.

On one occasion he was about to retire to bed when the sergeant brought in a prisoner.

"Hang it!" shouted the enraged Nash, "Am I not even allowed time to sleep? Get out of here!" The frightened sergeant dragged the prisoner away. Next morning when taking his customary walk Nash saw a body hanging from the gibbet at North-gate.

"Gatekeeper!" he called, "who is that fellow?" The gatekeeper explained that it was the body of the man he sentenced to be hanged on the previous evening. At first, Nash was puzzled and then the unfortunate consequence of his impatient expletive – "Hang it, man! Am I not even allowed time to sleep?" – dawned upon him. He reflected on the situation for a moment or two.

"Oh well," he said at last, "if he didn't deserve it this time, he probably would have some other time."

On another occasion a prisoner was brought before him just as he was about to have dinner. "Another rapparee?" he asked the sergeant.

"Yes, sir!" was the reply.

"Right," said Nash, "take him out and hang him now. I'll try him after I've had dinner."

Historian Bennet records a conversation he himself had with an elderly Bandon citizen concerning Nash. "Tim," I enquired, "did you ever hear of Provost Nash?"

"Ould Jack the Devil, is it?" said Tim. "Wisha, be gonnies, I did so." I then asked him why Nash had hanged so many people.

"Be gor," said he, "for being Papists." "But, suppose a man said he was not a Papist?" Here I thought I had old Tim.

"Ah be gorra," said he, "that wouldn't do him aither for then he'd hang him for tellin' lies."

Shaun Nash died in 1725 in his seventy-fifth year. So detested was he that his remains weren't interred in the family burial-place at Brinny in case they'd be exhumed and dishonoured by the local people. Under cover of night, the body was placed in an unmarked tomb in Kilbrogan Church. In West Cork, Shaun Nash, the hanging judge, will never be forgotten.

THE HOLY PLACES VANDALISED

Irish Independent, December 1979

To the Christian pilgrim seeking to follow in the footsteps of the Master, the Land of the Cross can present a puzzling and often frustrating picture.

While 2,000 years have not changed the message preached by Jesus in the villages of Judea and Galilee, the passing centuries have levelled these villages and rebuilt them and changed them till, quite often, only tradition now pinpoints the holy places that will forever be venerated and revered. And worse, well-meaning Christians down the ages have vandalised the simplicity of the holy places by erecting grandiose basilicas where simple shrines in the natural setting might well have been more appropriate.

Following the Way of Sorrow, along which Jesus bore his cross from the Place of Judgment to Calvary, the mind slips back easily over 2,000 years. The narrow streets, the ancient arches spanning the cobbled lanes, the colourfully robed Arabs, the laden donkeys, the pathetic poverty, this is surely where Jesus walked!

Here Veronica wiped the face of Jesus. The relentless sun beating on your head today is the same sun that beat on his bloodied brow 2,000 years ago. Jesus falls the third time. We kneel where he fell on the rough cobbles and pray. The tenth Station – Jesus is stripped of his garments . . .

But suddenly, somehow, we have left the bustle of the Arab markets and we are within the shadowy confines of the Church of the Holy Sepulchre. We are on Calvary – or so the guide tells us. But the Hill of Calvary is no more – this old church houses what is left of the traditional site of Christ's crucifixion and burial.

The ancient Hill of Calvary, revered by the followers of Jesus, was obliterated in 135 AD by a statue of Jupiter and an altar to the pagan goddess, Venus, placed there by the Roman Emperor Hadrian. Two hundred years later, under the Christian hand of the Byzantium Emperor Constantine, this pagan shrine was removed revealing again the sacred tomb of Christ. All extraneous rock was cut away, thus enabling a grandiose church to fit over the old tomb and mound. This church was destroyed and reinstated on at least two occasions and the restorations of 1049 have remained to this day.

The Church of the Holy Sepulcher is shared by five religious denominations: Roman Catholic, Greek, Coptic, Ethiopians and Armenians. Each group performs separate services, maintains distinct altars and chapels and even though they are, at present, engaged in a combined programme of repairs, jealousy and inter-denominational strife and rivalry have, at times, left the holy edifice in such a state of disrepair that it was in imminent danger of collapse. In the 1920s, only the emergency propping-up of the walls by the British Army saved the building from total collapse.

So the pilgrim who had hoped to climb the Hill of Calvary in the footsteps of Christ will be grievously disappointed. Calvary has been sucked into a vortex of jealousy and dispute, embellished with lamps and ornaments in the Greek Orthodox fashion, beautiful in its artificiality but, like the hill itself, its message of good tidings and joy has been obscured. Sadly, even on Calvary, Christian peoples have failed to come together in peace and hope.

For Christians the world over, no mountain holds more spiritual significance than the Mount of Olives. Here Jesus taught his disciples on the slopes overlooking the Temple; here he was taken captive, and from here he ascended into Heaven. On the lower slopes of the Mount of Olives there stands to this day a peaceful grove of ancient olive trees, their gnarled trunks and branches turned and twisted as if in endless agony. These old trees and their fruit, have given the place its name – the Garden of Gethsemane. It was here at Gethsemane that Jesus almost succumbed to his despair and sought to find a way of escape from his forthcoming passion and death. And it was while he prayed at the rock of agony that he overcame the weakness of his human flesh and accepted the divine will of the Father.

Nowadays, the garden is under the care of the Franciscan Brothers and, at first sight, that same puzzling sense of disappointment once again floods the pilgrim's heart – as on Calvary and in Bethlehem and in Nazareth and all the holy places, another palatial Church obliterates most of what was once the Garden of Agony. But a happy surprise awaits the pilgrim when he enters the church, now called the Church of All Nations. Architect Antonia Barluzi was surely inspired by Divine Providence when he used as his focal paint the grim outcrop of natural rock, which he allowed to protrude through the floor of the church in front of the main altar. Its total simplicity gives it a beauty beyond understanding. Here, at last, is something tangible from the life of Jesus, a reality from the ancient past. Here the pilgrim may kneel where Christ knelt and rest his forehead on the cold rock seeking the comfort that Christ sought. That bare rock, unadorned, almost hostile, transcends the ephemeral glitter and glamour of the man-made baubles and architectural artistry that despoil Calvary, Bethlehem and Nazareth.

Here, more than anywhere else in the Land of the Cross, the Master waits for those who wish to follow in his footsteps. From the rock in the Garden of Gethsemane they can go forward together in hope . . .

Leppin about in West Cork

RTÉ, *Sunday Miscellany*, December 2001

When it comes to the long jump or the high jump, I don't think any Olympic records were ever broken in West Cork. On the other hand, if we're talking about leppin – be it a high lep or a long lep – now there's a different thing altogether. In West Cork, you see, they never jump but they do be leppin all over the place all the time. And I'll tell you something else – we're not talking ordinary leps here. Oh no! We're talking big, big leps.

Take the pretty little village of 'Lep' on the road between Clonakilty and Skibbereen – the name is spelled L-E-A-P, of course, but like I said, in West Cork every leap is a lep so how did the village get such a distinctive name? Historian Daniel O'Donovan wrote in 1876: "At the upper end of Glandore harbour is a deep and dangerous gorge which cuts through the high road from Ross to the other parts of West Carbery. The gorge is here as steep as a flight of stairs so that no horse would ever attempt to jump it with courage."

One horse, which did attempt it, and attempted it successfully, was the horse of the local chieftain, O'Donovan. Pursued by English forces after the battle of Kinsale he found himself trapped before the gorge, 35 meters deep and 12 meters across.

Faced with the choice of the hangman's noose or the impossible jump, O'Donovan desperately put his horse to the gorge and with a wild "Helloo" that echoed all the way to the sea, he was up and over and safely away into the wilds of West Carbery.

Every summer thousands of tourists pass through Leap village, located beside this gorge and are, no doubt, mildly amused or even puzzled by the strange name and its quaint Irish pronunciation. The gorge itself, now bridged by the main road to Skibbereen, is choked with trees, wild shrubs and litter of all sorts and is barely visible. And as yet there is no sign to tell the tourist of the mighty lep that named the village and booked O'Donovan his place in the proud history – not to mention the geography – of West Cork.

On the other hand, just outside Bantry on the Glengarriff road there is a plaque, that marks the spot where a very reverend gentleman is supposed to have landed when he jumped his horse from the top of the mountain three miles away. This prodigious jump is known as the Priest's Leap, and according to the information on the plaque, the priest, like O'Donovan, was forced to make the leap to escape capture by priest-hunting English soldiers. And, says the plaque, the marks on the nearby flat rock are the prints made by the horse's hooves when it landed.

"If you believe that you'd believe anything," said an elderly lady who had paused to pray at the plaque on her way home from the ten o'clock Mass. "The good priest wasn't ridin' any horse, and he wasn't being chased by the English nather."

According to her, the holy man was walking from Kenmare to Bantry to visit a friend and he was still on the summit of the mountain when word came that his friend had taken gravely ill and was already at death's door.

Fearing that he might arrive too late to administer the last sacraments, the priest knelt down and prayed for heavenly guidance. Then, filled with a surge of divine energy, he stretched out his arms and leaped from the summit of the mountain, landing safely on a flat rock just outside his dying friend's cottage – and not a leap of three miles as folk-lore would have it but a huge leap of 12 miles. And the marks on the rock, the lady insisted, are quite obviously not the hoof-prints of a horse but the prints made by the holy priest's hands and knees.

And, as if to finally tie up any loose ends or dispel any lingering doubts I might have about the authenticity of her version of this historic event, she pointed up at the dark brooding mountain: "Shur, for God's sake, what class of an eejit would believe that an oul horse could lep 12 miles?"

And even in West Cork we have no answer to that one.

DAY RETURN

Woman's Way, June 1989

"How old is old, Mam?" my only son, Tommy, asked me, slightly annoyed, when he rang from Australia.

He wanted me to travel out there on an all expenses-paid holiday – he would foot all the bills – and though I so dearly wanted to see the two little granddaughters I had never met, I just couldn't face that journey alone.

"I'm too old for it, Tommy," I explained. That's when he demanded to know how old was old. I didn't answer him. When my husband, Jack, died four years ago and left me alone, that's when I got old.

I thought of Tommy's question again a few weeks later when I sat on a rock beside the beach at Granthaven, and I smiled. Lord knows there was little enough to smile at that day in Granthaven. It was in this little seaside village that I met Jack when we were young students, on holiday over 45 years before.

When the doctor told me that I needed a change and a rest, my mind had flown back over those 45 years and I had packed my bag on impulse and taken a train to Granthaven the following morning.

The trip was a mistake – the fleeting years had found what I had almost forgotten, and Granthaven had changed. Not the village itself, mind you, you can't erase the stamp of centuries with a few flickering neon signs and a crazy-golf course.

The pub where I first met Jack, that glorious old pub where the white-jerseyed fishermen had drunk their evening pints, had gamely tried to retain some of its old-world charm. However, the garish juke-box, plastic fittings and a blond barman with his long hair tied back in a ribboned bow, clashed uneasily with the old oak bar and smoke-blacked rafters of a different age. The fishermen were gone, and so were the pint jugs. But the day-trippers down from the city were there in their shorts and their T-shirts and their noisy chatter seemed to mock the ghosts of long ago.

Hopefully, I wandered to the beach. That, if anything, was worse. Above the white strand, a funfair had sprung up. It was a sprawling dump of tents and huts, with dodgems and bingo and people shouting and bells ringing.

What used to be a charming cottage overlooking the beach had been vulgarly renovated. The white-washed front was replaced by two big plate-glass windows filled with cheap souvenirs and lurid postcards. The owners sold ice cream, soft drinks, and candyfloss, and they gave noise away, free.

Oh, that noise! The music blared all day from a cluster of loudspeakers on the roof, echoing and re-echoing across the beach, bouncing back and forth between the grey cliffs, a throbbing rattle of heavy metal and pop.

That's when I saw her first and I smiled that first smile. She looked so different, so completely out of place. The spindly legs, like brown straws, jutted down from a pair of men's rolled-up trousers. Her blouse was of plain white silk, secured at the neck by a gold horse shoe brooch. Heavy gold rings hung from her ears and a flowered, knotted scarf shrouded a lean, leathery face wrinkled by years of smiles. She was like a gypsy from a different age.

"Pleasant day for the seaside," she offered, her darting blue eyes taking me in at a glance. "I hope you're enjoying it."

"It's not the Granthaven I had hoped to find," I replied sadly. "It's not the Granthaven of 45 years ago where I first met my husband . . . "

"You were here 45 years ago?" It wasn't really a question – she was just organising the facts in her own mind, getting everything in its place. "And this is your first visit since – since. . . ?" She couldn't find the right words but her waving arm took it all in again.

"The change is very much for the worst," I said, glancing round. "Jack – my husband – he'd have hated to find it like this . . . " Our eyes met for a few seconds. There was no need to explain.

"You're right," she said after a minute, "the change is for the worst."

I smiled at her solemnity. "Well, it's not all that unusual, I suppose. I should have known not to come back – it's happening all along the coast, all over the place. The quiet old places have been taken over..."

"Mind you, the village is very prosperous now," she said. "The people are much better off and there's work for the youngsters – they don't have to go away now." She was watching me out of the corner of her eye, wondering if I was agreeing with her. She must have felt that I wasn't convinced. "But, like you, I often wonder if it was all worth the price we paid. The young people don't appreciate the good things – what we think are the good things. And of course we don't appreciate what they think are the good things . . . " Again she waved expressively towards the funfair and lapsed into silence.

There was a lull in the awful music. "Maybe the machine is broken," I said hopefully. "Even if they'd turn it down a bit . . . "

"No such luck," she smiled. "Leo – he's the man in charge – he's getting a bit deaf now, you see and he's probably only changing the tapes." She was right. A torrent of rock 'n' roll hit our ears.

"You know something," she said, "it's done me a lot of good meeting you – to meet someone who appreciated the old Granthaven. Some days here as I wander along the beach thinking to myself and worrying, I'm not always sure." Her eyes held mine unwaveringly. "But you can't stand still in time, you know, you must keep abreast of what's happening, you mustn't always be looking back. That's what being alive is all about..."

A wail of unhappy frustration drowned out her voice. A stout harassed man with a red face, his braces over his shirt, was waddling barefoot along the strand with two small boys in tow. He aimed a swipe at the bigger one.

"Stop pullin at me trousers, will ye? And I've told youse a dozen times that ye're not going next nor near the water till the Mammy gets here. And if I hear one more peep out of youse . . . "

My companion was already on her feet. No knight in shining armour ever approached a fair lady in distress as chivalrously as she approached the stout man. And no fair lady in distress ever succumbed to charm as readily as he succumbed to hers. A few words, a beaming smile, and my gypsy friend was heading for the welcoming waves, two happy little boys by her side.

She stopped and turned suddenly, remembering me in my unhappiness. "Remember what I said about keeping up," she called, "and I'll mention what you said about the music to Leo – about turning it down, I mean . . . " And like an ocean liner being joggled by two tiny tugs, she was dragged happily to the sea.

An hour later when the train pulled out of Granthaven, I was on it, heading back for home. I could still see the old gypsy lady picking her way along the beach. I smiled my sympathy. I, at least, could up and leave – she was stuck with it. A shirt-sleeved man beside me pointed down to the beach.

"See that old lady there – the one with the trousers rolled up?" I nodded. "Richest woman around these parts, she is – could buy and sell the lot of us. Saw the signs years ago and sold the husband's fishing boat and now she owns the lot – funfair, the pub, the disco, the whole works."

I stared at him, open-mouthed. "And the ice cream parlour?" I asked at last, "The place where they play that terrible music?" He nodded vigorously.

"Owns that too – her husband, Leo, he runs it now since he gave up the fishing. Likes to make people happy, she does. She'll go to any lengths to do that – even does a bit of fortune-telling on the side..."

The train hooter blared, to merge for a moment with Leo's music. Down on the beach, the small figure looked up and waved. On impulse I stood up and leaned out of the window and waved back. It was then, I think, that I realised what she had been trying to do. Granthaven hadn't changed at all – it was just flowing with the tide, keeping up, staying abreast. It was I who was stuck in the past, and time had passed me by. I made up my mind there and then.

"Thank you," I whispered, still waving and not feeling one bit embarrassed though the people in the carriage were looking at me curiously. "Thank you, my friend, I'll come to see you when I get back from Australia and we'll have a good long chat."

Soon the small figure faded out of sight, still tidying up, still being helpful. I sat down but a sudden thought brought me to my feet again. "And, oh please," I whispered out the window, "don't say anything to Leo about the music . . ."

THE FORGOTTEN WIVES OF IRELAND'S WILD GEESE

Ireland's Own, September 1982

Many chapters of history are devoted to the proud exploits of Ireland's Wild Geese; those exiled soldiers of fortune who served with distinction in the armies of Europe. Writing about the period, in 1867, Charles Smith says that the valour of Irish soldiers was well-known, and between 1661 and 1664 more than fifty-four thousand Irishmen were shipped abroad, most of whom would never see their native land again. Little attention, however, is given to the sad plight of the wives and families they left behind.

After the Treaty of Limerick when Sarsfield and his army were forced to take ship to France, there were harrowing scenes at the Shannon dockside. Crowds of screaming, sobbing women were ruthlessly beaten back when they tried to join their departing sons and husbands. "It was," wrote Historian Bennett, "as if the end of their world had come upon them."

And so it had. As early as 1645 Lord Broghill of Bandon, a trusted lieutenant of Oliver Cromwell, decided that, whatever the cost, he must, as he sanctimoniously put it, "save such unfortunate women from possible immorality."

He then ordered that: "Irish women now being too numerous after the recent wars and therefore exposed to prostitution, should be sold to merchants and transported to Virginia, New England, Jamaica or other countries where they may support themselves by their labours."

These women, he suggested, should be arrested anywhere within 20 miles of Bandon and shipped out at Kinsale. "It is not a difficult task at this time," he informed Cromwell to procure plenty of females of marriageable age and not past breeding. "There are crowds of such, young widows and deserted wives wandering about in the vicinity of Bandon without any visible means of support."

To carry out his plan he sent agents to England, and contracted with Messrs Sellick and Leader of Bristol to furnish them with two hundred and fifty women of the Irish nation for transplantation into slavery. And so the first batch consisting of thousands of Irish women were shipped across the ocean to sweat out their lives in the heat and misery of the sugar-cane plantations of the West Indies.

Happily however, not all the deserted women of Cork allowed themselves to be kidnapped and forced into slavery. Historian Dr Gibson describes how Joan Barry, a widow and the mother of David McPhillip Barry, later a Captain in Sarsfield's army, twice led bands of women, as many as 400 strong, into the thriving town of Clonakilty and ransacked every house that was in it. The first incursion was in 1642.

"There was no opposing these Amazons," claimed Gibson, and he went on to record that "with one weapon in their fist and another between their teeth, they could bewilder as well as pummel their antagonists. Quickly they overspread proud Clonakilty. Like a swarm of locusts they pitched upon everything. The curiosity and pillaging proclivities of Joan Barry's Red Shanks, as they were called, left nothing escape them. These unwomanly women stuffed everything into their bottomless pockets and when they walked off they left many a full heart behind them, and an empty shelf."

Unfortunately, the efforts of Joan Barry and her followers to evade arrest came to nothing. Wherever they hid in the hills or forests of West Cork, Broghill's soldiers searched them out relentlessly and shipped them to slavery in Virginia and the West Indies.

And unlike their husbands and sons, famed across Europe in song and in story, there are no monuments in foreign fields to honour their memory or tell of their sacrifice. At best, they will be remembered as the forgotten wives of Ireland's Wild Geese.

Nightlife in Moscow

Irish Press, April 1979

Now that the Soviet Union has thrown open her embracing arms to the ordinary tourist as well as the faithful party cardholder, what may the tourist expect, and how will he be entertained?

Moscow by day is an exercise in cultural saturation. The tourist will be overawed by the grandeur, magnificence and sheer beauty of the Kremlin, its museums and cathedrals. He will be overwhelmed by the vastness and depth of the Exhibition Of Economic Achievement, and bored stiff by the monotonous and hackneyed propaganda of the Museum of the Workers' Revolution. And at night? Where can the average Irishman who finds himself in Moscow turn to in this mysterious and eerie city of the Tsars and the revolutions?

Where, in fact, does the average Muscovite, his work quota successfully completed, spend his celebration evening? The guidebooks all bear pictures depicting night scenes in Moscow and captioned: "At night the neon signs of cafes and restaurants light up – here Muscovites meet friends, celebrate birthdays and wedding anniversaries..."

This is all very nice for our Muscovite friends. Very nice too for the tourist who has been detailed to attend the famous Bolshoi Ballet by Intourist, the Official Russian Travel Agency, the only people able to procure tickets for such delectable outings. Or they may send him to the Moscow State Circus. But what if you haven't booked for such optional extras when you paid out your money in Dublin? Where will you go tonight? To put it bluntly, where would a fella get a good pint, with maybe a bar or two of an owld song thrown in (nothing cultural like)? I mean, what's really going down in Moscow town tonight?

While there are no bars or pubs as we know them here in Ireland, and certainly no singing pubs or swinging nightclubs there are some very fine luxury hotels where you can get a drink – if you are a resident. And if you are not a resident there is no way that you'll get past the door-man, even at eleven o'clock in the morning, not to mind eleven o'clock at night.

From about seven o'clock in the evening the guitars and the drums beat out. The Hotel Ukraine, for instance, has its own resident band led by a suave swinging gent named Alexander, and there is dancing space between the tables in the restaurant. The tempo is probably as hot as anything you'll hear from a western group, the drummer will look as hypnotically lost as any western drummer, the guitarist will writhe and groan with the same sincere enthusiasm of his western brother, and the singer will, undoubtedly, hold his own in any class though he does appear happier when handling Russian folk songs. Cultural breeding – especially Russian cultural breeding – is hard to beat.

Saturday night is when everything is happening. Group wedding parties are allowed in the hotels. They follow the same pattern as wedding parties in Irish hotels. The brides in their long white gowns and the grooms, self-conscious and ruddy faced in their new suits, 'freak out' in a subdued imitation of the swinging action of a western disco scene. And Mom and Dad and Ma-in-law and Da-in-law, and the uncles and aunts and the cousins join in the communal fun. Large bottles of unlabelled beer and exotically labelled and very expensive bottles of wine and vodka are sold by a lady sitting alone at a well-stocked table. There is no bar as we know it. No chance here of having one put on the slate. No slate. No smile. Pay your money. Get your drink and get on with being happy. There is nobody drunk, though everybody seems to be happily tipsy. The high price tags on the bottles see to that.

Then comes eleven o'clock and bang goes the shutters on the nightlife of Moscow. Everything just stops with absolute Russian finality, and everybody goes home. Cinderella, in this swinging town, is no tarty gad-about who burns the candle at both ends. The honeymoons are over. There is work to be done tomorrow, work quotas to be filled and quickly the well-lit streets and boulevards empty themselves of their scant traffic. The walkers who had filled the streets from early dawn dwindle to the odd lost and perplexed tourist and the ever-watchful policeman.

Maybe the time has come for somebody to open a few good old-fashioned pubs along Gorky Street and then the sulky Russian bear might growl a little less and smile a little more. A 'Rasputin's Razzmatazz' or a 'Brezhnev's Bar and Barbecue' in downtown Red Square would probably attract more customers than Lenin's dreary old Mausoleum. And surely that wouldn't be a bad thing?

LOOKING BACK

Woman's Way, April 1987

This is it – I'm here! Now I'm going to sort out the problems that have haunted my 13 years of marriage to Barry.

Kate parked her Mini opposite Sheridan's Antique Shop. The narrow street rolling through the picturesque old village of Manway, the small green, the stone bridge, it was all exactly as she remembered it.

Through the car window she could see the sign swinging in the soft breeze over the shop door. It still creaked and groaned, but somehow, the display window seemed smaller. Even so, she could clearly see the inside of the shop cluttered with all shapes and sizes of antique furniture, pictures and bric-a-brac that Michael Sheridan gathered with loving care from all over the country. Her heart was pounding silently as she waited for Michael's tall figure to appear behind the counter.

Thirteen years ago today, she and Barry were married in the small church just up the road. For three years before that she had worked in this thriving little antique shop. She had been engaged to its owner, Michael Sheridan. And then, in a frenzied whirlwind of romance, her whole world was turned upside down as Barry swept her off her feet. He had simply been passing through and had stopped when he spotted a replica of a Chinese Ming vase in the window. It was love at first sight and they were married three months later.

Kate caught her breath as a white-coated figure moved into view and breathed easily again when she saw it was an assistant. She watched the blonde figure moving around the shop, checking prices here, dusting items there and wondered if that was how she had looked to Barry when he peered through that same window and saw her for the first time.

"You took my breath away," he had whispered to her during their first dinner together that night. "I stopped for what turned out to be an imitation Ming Vase and I found the most beautiful, wonderful treasure of all times. I'll never forget today as long as I live . . . " She had remembered those words this morning when she sat opposite him at breakfast wondering if he had forgotten that today was their thirteenth wedding anniversary. And when finally he gave her the usual perfunctory kiss on the forehead and drove off to the office, she accepted that he had completely forgotten. Things had changed she thought; a lot of the wonderful magic of 13 years ago had gone out of their marriage.

Are you going to sit in the car all day looking hopefully through the window or are you going into that shop to try to sort out your life?

Bracing herself for whatever might be ahead, Kate got out of the car and walked towards the shop. A clattering peal from the bell rang out when she pushed the door open. Over the last 13 years, in her daydreams, Kate had walked through that door hundreds of times and now she wondered how she could ever have forgotten the bell. She looked up at it in startled surprise. The blonde assistant, sitting at the mahogany table that served as a cash desk, smiled at her.

"It is rather loud, isn't it? But you get used to it." Her eyebrows lifted in question. "May I help you or do you just want to look around?"

Kate smiled. Nothing had changed – that was Michael's standard greeting to all his customers and the first instruction he gave her when he employed her was that she should do likewise. That was how she had greeted Barry on that day long ago – the day he said he'd never forget . . .

"I'll just have a look around, please," Kate smiled. She saw with a rush of relief that there was nobody in Michael's office at the back of the shop. "You have such lovely things . . . "

Of course today's anniversary wasn't the first one Barry had forgotten. Mind you, he always arrived a day or two later, full of repentance and laden with flowers and a card and a present. She knew too that if there was a problem in their marriage, it wasn't just Barry's bad memory – it was the gnawing, nagging doubt that lurked in the dim recesses of her own mind.

She walked slowly up and down the familiar aisles of the shop with all the nostalgic aromas of old wood and leather wafting about her, oh my goodness, she gasped silently, that floorboard outside Michael's office still creaks! It was then that she allowed those hidden doubts to flood into the open and she was shocked at the impact they created within her.

You rushed into marriage with Barry! she told herself. If you had waited and thought about it and given yourself time to make a more rational decision you'd have married Michael, dear dependable Michael whom you knew and loved for so many years. Your marriage to Barry was a mistake. Your real life is here with Michael.

She tried angrily to dismiss these thoughts. Even if the earlier magic was gone out of their marriage, even if thoughts of Michael Sheridan occupied her daydreams more and more, there was still a mature contentment, an acceptance of her role as a successful businessman's wife. And when the twins were home from school, the house was full of love and life. Barry just forgot a few anniversaries, for goodness sake; she told herself – that's not what's putting our marriage in danger.

She picked up a vase, vaguely admiring the way the pale sunshine picked out the delicate porcelain patterns. She sighed. If only she had never placed that imitation Ming on display in the window all those years ago. If only . . . if only . . .

"What a beautiful brooch you're wearing!" Kate hadn't noticed the assistant coming up beside her. "It's Victorian, isn't it?" Kate's hand fluttered to the brooch. She had quite forgotten that she pinned it on this morning.

"It – it's broken," she said cloaking her sudden confusion. "I can't take it off – the catch needs mending. It was a wedding present . . . " She smiled politely ignoring the assistant's suggestion that they might be able to repair it for her.

No way could she allow anybody in this shop to open it! There was too much of her past locked up in there – hers and Michael's.

That morning, when Barry had left the house, she did what she had been doing more and more during the last few years. She took the leather-bound wedding album out of the drawer in the sideboard and thumbed through it until she came to the group photograph taken on the church steps. There had been 44 guests: 27 invited by her and 17 invited by Barry – his mother and father, his only sister and seven members of the football club, and their girlfriends.

In the back row of the photograph on the left-hand side, the tall, slim figure of Michael Sheridan seemed to stand slightly apart from the group. When she invited him to the wedding she hadn't really expected him to come. And when he joined the noisy boisterous queue waiting to kiss the blushing bride, her heart had done a little flutter as his lips touched her cheek. He whispered huskily that he wished her all the happiness in the world and he slipped a small packet into her hand which, for reasons she still couldn't fathom, she kept hidden in her bouquet till she got a chance to open it in private.

Later in the evening she cried a little when she found the packet contained a small antique heart-shaped brooch of delicate silver with 'I shall always love you' engraved on the back. When she pressed the small catch at the side it opened and one section held a photograph of herself. The other compartment was starkly empty. Often over the years she had thought of putting Barry's photograph into the empty space but she never had. This morning, on impulse, she got a small scissors from her bag and cut out Michael's head from the group photograph. She snipped it carefully into a heart shape and fitted it into the brooch.

"There," she said aloud to herself. "I've done it at last. Now I'll drive down to Manway and face the ghost that has haunted my marriage for 13 years . . . "

The clang of the bell made her jump and she whirled around.

"I'm back, darling!" Michael Sheridan stood holding the door open. Kate's heart leaped in delight. She had heard that familiar greeting so often in the past when Michael returned from some auction or sale. She made to move towards him and as she did a boy of about ten pushed past him carrying a brown cardboard box full of books.

"We got the books, Mum," he called, a delighted smile

creasing his chubby face. "Dad was great – he outbid everybody there and he says they're worth twice the price we paid for them . . . " Michael ruffled his son's hair playfully. The blonde assistant came out of the office to greet them. Putting one arm around the boy's shoulders, she reached up to kiss Michael on the cheek. Kate turned her back abruptly and pretended to be engrossed in a painting. Her heart was pounding and she felt the colour rushing to her cheeks.

During the last 13 years, she had often imagined herself coming into this shop and meeting Michael again. Sometimes he had swept her into his arms and held her to him. Other times he was cold and a little aloof at first but when she explained that marrying Barry had been a terrible mistake he understood and kissed her in loving forgiveness. It had never, never occurred to her that he might have met somebody else.

The three went into the office. Kate could see Michael's face in the gilt mirror in front of her. His brown hair was a little thinner, his face much more gaunt than she remembered it. And suddenly Kate realised to her shock and surprise that the only thought in her head was that the silly little moustache Michael Sheridan was sporting didn't suit him one bit. It was sort of – squiggly. It really made him look quite silly. She'd never have allowed him to grow it, that's for sure!

She closed her eyes for a few seconds, her nails biting into her cold palms, an almost uncontrollable giggle forming in her throat. And then realisation flooded over her – the tender love that her memory had held all those years hadn't been anything other than that – a loving, tender memory.

She rang Barry's office as soon as she got home. She wasn't quite sure what she wanted to tell him – she only knew that she needed to talk to him, to hear his voice.

"Hello, darling," she heard at last and her heart did a little skip. "Where are you? You were gone when I got back with the flowers and things . . . " Kate's forehead wrinkled in surprise.

"Flowers? What flowers?" She heard Barry's throaty chuckle.

"You think I forgot our wedding anniversary, don't you?"

Out of the corner of her eye she saw the beautiful colours of a bouquet of flowers in the imitation Ming vase on the dining-room table. There were long-neck irises mixed with golden daffodils and spicy carnations and a card and a slim package that she knew contained jewellery.

"I said nothing this morning because I wanted to bring you freshly cut flowers to show that my love for you is as fresh today as it was when I first saw you on that little shop where you worked," he said poetically. "Do you remember that shop, Kate?"

Kate was laughing through her tears. She unpinned the brooch from her jacket and eased out Michael's photograph. She looked at it, stroking it tenderly with her thumb.

"Remember it, darling," she whispered. "How could I ever forget? Why, there was even a time when I thought I was in love with the owner. He was such a nice man..."

A TOUCH OF HISTORY

The Irish Times, November 1988

A wine-stained paper napkin with the name *Elizabeth Dobryuska* scribbled in biro, her Warsaw telephone number and a roughly drawn map of Ireland with the Northern six-county area heavily outlined is all I have now to remind me of an unexpected dinner in the Czechoslovak town of Olomouc in central Moravia.

It was a beautiful September afternoon when, by happy chance, three groups of tourists, mostly from Eastern Europe, came together in Olomouc. I was the only Western traveller among them and, as things turned out, that day was one of the highlights of a very pleasant tour.

Olomouc is the seventh largest city in Czechoslovakia and its central part has now been declared a preserved area housing Gothic, Renaissance and Baroque architectural treasures. St Nicholas's Cathedral, St Michael's Church, the Church of Our Lady of the Snows and the Church of St Maurice, form a triangle of ancient architectural monuments that date back to the twelfth and sixteenth centuries. The fifteenth-century Town Hall in the main square has a very beautiful portal and its north side houses a large astronomical clock standing gable high. Opposite the Town Hall is an elaborate bronze sculpture of the Holy Trinity blending with the picturesque Hercules and Caesar fountains.

The cobbled square is a haven for tourists, reaching back into the distant history of a well-preserved town that was established in the second half of the eleventh century.

The organised walking tour of the central area left us ready for dinner at six o'clock, a little early perhaps by Irish standards but in Czechoslovakia, where city streets empty by 10.30 p.m. and fill again at 6.00 a.m. when workers start flooding to their factories, nightlife begins and finishes early.

It was in the colourful Restaurant Zenith that I found myself seated with a Professor from Belgrade University and a beautiful Polish lady, Elizabeth Dobryuska, a member of the Department of Foreign Trade in Warsaw. The traditional Czech dinner of goulash soup, roast pork and sauerkraut, washed down with vodka and a local Moravian wine, heady and strong, was but a tasty prelude to a wonderful evening's entertainment.

A nearby wine village had put its wares on display for their tourist visitors and a 12-strong choir of local men and women, in traditional Moravian costumes sang and danced for us, recreating the atmosphere of the simple village in which they spend their lives tending the precious vines. We drank and we danced with them, we joined in their song and we tasted their wines, a choice of 425 varieties in all, and we sang some more.

It was then that the Polish lady, resting between dances, said in her halting throaty English how lucky I was to be out of Ireland, away from the constant bombing and fighting. The Yugoslav Professor nodded in agreement: "We see so much on our television screens – Ireland and the Lebanon, year after year of war, war, war. How do the people bear it?"

And that accounts for the hastily drawn map of Ireland on my table napkin with the six counties of the North heavily outlined. There, in a crowded, noisy restaurant, far behind the Iron Curtain, I tried to explain the troubled history of Ireland to highly educated people from Poland and Yugoslavia, both of whom, as children, had endured the horror of occupation by Hitler's legions and who were now full of sympathy for me that I should have to live for so long under what they saw as similar conditions. I gave them the facts and figures but, while they listened politely, there was vague air of disbelief. "That is not the position as we understand it," Elizabeth Dobryuska told me "That is not how it is presented on our television screens," said the professor from Yugoslavia.

The band struck up and the waiters served some more wine and we put all talk of history behind us. And later that evening we went our separate ways. But now I think back and I wonder about them, and I wonder too what is history in this modern age. A waiter in our Prague hotel asked me what I thought of the Russian soldiers in Olomouch and was very surprised when I told him that I hadn't seen any. He came back to me later with a knowing smile: "Olomouc has the biggest garrison of Russian soldiers in all Czechoslovakia," he whispered. "They even have shops reserved exclusively for their use but on the days the tourist buses come to town the soldiers are confined to barracks so that foreigners do not see them."

And that, perhaps, helps to explain what history is about – now you are allowed to see it, now you are not, and its ugliness, like its beauty is in what the perceiver is allowed to behold. As for me and Olomouch and its Russian occupation troops, all I've got now is a paper napkin with the map of Ireland and the name and telephone number of a beautiful Polish woman from behind the Iron Curtain who was very sad for me because I had to live in war-torn Ireland. And, of course, I have my memories. And, unlike history, nobody can meddle with them...

Sodom, Cork and Gomorrah

RTÉ, *Sunday Miscellany*, June 1995

That the name of the fair City of Cork – The Holy Ground, for God's sake could be coupled in the same sentence with the names of the evil cities of Sodom and Gomorrah seems beyond belief! But so it is when Historian Dr Caulfield in his History of Cork quotes from what he refers to as "a rare tract from the library of the British Museum". This tract carries the cumbersome title *The Prognostication of the Battle of the Birds relating to the Lamentable Burning of the City of Cork by Thunder and Lightning.*

According to Caulfield, the sun was shining brilliantly in Cork on the morning of 7 October 1621. The good citizens of the city were going about their business when suddenly an enormous cloud darkened the sky. Soon the curiosity of the people turned to fright, and then terror, when a strange rustling noise emanated from the cloud that by now overshadowed the whole city. Then the cloud was seen to divide, one part moving towards the east quarter of the sky and the other towards the west. Only then did the terrified citizens realise that the darkness that now totally obscured the light of the sun was caused by huge flocks of starlings blacking out the sky. Here Caulfield quotes from the old manuscript:

"At last when the sides found themselves complete,

both armies of starlings made a prodigious outcry, which however did not last long, for in an instance all the birds were seen to arise in the air and pushed at each other with such a terrible rustling that the people stood amazed. In a short time after they were engaged many came tumbling down into the city and in the fields. Some had their wings broken, others their necks, others their legs; a great many had their eyes picked out. All day they battled and so many thousands of them were tumbling in the streets that they had to be carried away in carts and barrows."

The tract then goes on to suggest that this bloody battle of the starlings was but a warning of much worse horrors to come and goes on to describe the terrible events of the following year, in May 1622, when fire came down from heaven and consumed Cork.

"The last day of May being Friday, betwixt eleven and twelve of the clock, the clouds over the city began to gather thick, which caused such a darkness in their houses, that the inhabitants were amazed to behold such sudden darkness. These dark clouds seemed to muster together and to descend by degrees near to the city. Whilst the inhabitants stood thus wondering and in fear, suddenly they heard a terrible clap of thunder, and at the same instant they saw a dreadful lightning with flames of fire break out of the clouds and fall upon the city at the same instant at the East and at the highest part of the city. And at the very same place where the starlings began their battle and where they first fell down being killed in the fight, there a fire began with horrible flames. And the helpless citizens were turning their eyes this way and that way, where sometimes their habitations were, where they had goods, wives and children, brothers and sisters and fathers and mothers, cousins and friends and all either consumed or in danger to be consumed by fire. And what the battle of the birds did presage and prognosticate fell out too true and doleful in the utter ruin and consumption of a rich and wealthy city.'"

In a rather bazaar attempt to explain these strange and tragic happenings, the British Museum tract then goes on to harshly compare Cork with the cities of Sodom and Gomorrah:

"Albeit I compare this city with Sodom and Gomorrah, it is not in respect of the sins, but in the respect of the heavy hand of God showed in like degrees. No question but Cork had her sins which provoked the heavy hand of God to fall so heavily upon her. However, unlike the sinners of Sodom and Gomorrah, whose sin is well known, it was the sin of usury, that cheerful daughter of covetousness, that the citizens of Cork were long noted for, and to such an extent as to exceed any other city in the King's Dominions. And for such sins the cities of Sodom and Gomorrah were not more suddenly or more deservedly consumed with fire than this cursed city of Cork was."

A SEVENTEENTH-
CENTURY WHODUNNIT

RTÉ, *Sunday Miscellany*, May 1997

In 1667 the picturesque West Cork village of Rosscarbery became the scene of what was probably Ireland's first whodunnit. It involved all the classic ingredients of the genre with an elderly parson, a barren wife, a butler and a church sexton, playing the lead roles. And whatever about a prurient press of the day – if there was such a thing in 1667 – the matter definitely attracted the attention of Ireland's leading eighteenth-century historians. Dr Smith in his thesis, *The Present State of the County of Cork*, Bennett in his *History of Bandon* and Dr Roche in *A History of West Cork*, all considered it worthy of record, and they all left varying accounts of the events. But taken together, and with a wink here and a nudge there, it all adds up to a rather strange tale.

When the Normans arrived in Rosscarbery, the Benedictine monks founded a priory on the south side of the village. To the east of this building stood the original St Fachna's Cathedral. This cathedral was demolished and rebuilt as a Protestant Cathedral in 1612. It is still in use today; half the building being a museum and the other half a place of worship. And it was to here, in the year 1667 that the body of Mrs Goodman, wife of the Rev. Richard Goodman, vicar of Ballymodan, Bandon, was brought for burial in the family vault.

The Goodmans, Smith tells us, had been happily

married for nearly 15 years. Apart from the occasional attack of the vapours, so prevalent in genteel female circles in those days, Mrs Goodman had always been in excellent health. Unfortunately, to the great disappointment of her elderly husband, she had never been able to produce the son who he fervently prayed would bless their union. In fact, at this time he accepted the unhappy fact that Mrs Goodman was infertile and had given up all hopes of a blessed event.

Then an unexpected quirk of fate changed everything. Dr Dive Downes, the Protestant Bishop of Cork, decided to make a tour of his vast diocese and invited Rev. Richard Goodman to accompany him. Rev. Goodman gladly accepted, but because his wife seemed to be coming down much more frequently with the vapours, he decided to hire a butler to relieve her of the burden of running the busy household. She could then, in his missionary absence, devote more caring time to the welfare of his parishioners. And so the bishop and Rev. Goodman set off on their journey and Mrs Goodman and the new butler shouldered the duties of running the busy parish.

After a three-week journey through the diocese The Rev. Goodman shared in the delight of his Bishop at the success of their mission. But there was even greater joy to come. A month after his return, Mrs Goodman proudly confided to her husband that she was pregnant, and she felt it in her very bones that the baby would be a boy. Their cup of happiness was overflowing. And for reasons of economy and their changing circumstances, she told him, she had this morning dispensed with the services of the butler and hired a housekeeper instead. Then, sadly, just a week later, no doubt overcome with the joy of her pregnancy, she succumbed to an attack of the vapours and lapsed into a trance. That very evening she was pronounced dead.

Here the plot thickens. Dr Roche, in his *A History of Cork*, writes of Rosscarbery Cathedral: "It was in a vault in this building that a Mrs Goodman, wife of the Rev. Richard Goodman was buried, and concerning whom it is related that the sexton, being anxious to make his own a very valuable ring which was on one of her fingers, entered the tomb at night and in his efforts to possess himself of the coveted jewel, awoke her out of the state of epilepsy she was in . . . "

Referring to the same incident, Historian Bennett suggests that it was the butler, angry at the treatment meted out to him by Mrs Goodman, who had attempted to compensate himself by stealing the ring, and in the process revived her and unwittingly saved her life. The butler – or was it the sexton? – fled in terror and Mrs Goodman managed to make her way out of the vault and returned to the arms of her shocked husband.

Despite her harrowing ordeal, she later gave birth to a healthy son, John. Unfortunately, the longed-for son and heir didn't bring the couple the happiness they expected. According to Smith, he grew up to be a vagabond, spending all his days in the taverns of Innishannon and Bandon cadging drink by telling in graphic detail how he was the only person ever to be born after his mother had been buried in her grave. He died in Cork, aged eighty.

In Additional Notes to Smith's *The Present State of the County of Cork* published in 1893, W. A. Coppinger states that the Rev. Goodman died soon after his wife returned from the dead. She subsequently married a man named Longfield and bore him a son.

And so, three hundred years later, weighing up the various notes, accounts and historical data left to us by the historians, and sifting carefully through the circumstantial evidence, one can only come to the inevitable conclusion that whatever was done – if anything was done – the butler done it!

THE GIFT

Radio Eireann, October 1950

Blind Billy forgave me today and the cold wind whipping through the bleak cemetery swept the clouds of sorrow from my soul. For 60 long years I had waited for that – 60 long years sailing the oceans of the world, master of my ship, a proud and successful man, but ever tormented by the memory of what I did to the only friend of my youth. I killed Blind Billy. I killed him because I loved him too much!

I'll never forget the first time I met Blind Billy. The setting sun had flung long shadows across the evening when he came tap-tap-tapping his way into my young life. A once tall figure, now bowed with age, his sightless eyes searched the deep blackness ahead as he paused uncertainly at my aunt's front door. Sensing my silent presence, his hand reached out to touch me. First my shoulder, then fluttering like a bird to my head, his sensitive fingers explored the angles of my face. I stood there stiffly, a little frightened, a little bewildered.

"You seem a nice young lad." The voice was gentle, reassuring. "Tell me, now, which would be Number 27?"

I was shrinking back from the hovering hand. "Missus. Missus Burke?" I stuttered. He sensed my fear.

"You're not afraid of owld Blind Billy, are you, lad?"

I eyed the tattered raincoat, the old bowler hat and the broken boots. "Naw, I'm not afraid of you." I was even beginning to feel a little cocky. "And everybody knows Missus Burke. She's always drunk and the police arrested her . . . " The hand closed over my mouth.

"What's your name, lad? How old are you?"

I struggled to free myself. "Jamsie Mangan," I said "and I'm nearly ten . . . "

Those blind eyes bored through me, but the gentleness of his lined face was reassuring.

"That's no way for a young fella to be talking, Jamsie. If you have nothing good to say about your friends, say nothing." He patted my head paternally. "Now, let's be off, you and me, to the good Mrs Burke. I hear she has an owld room to let out cheap . . . "

And so our friendship was born: Blind Billy, seventy-five, unloved and alone, and I, just ten, living with an aunt who didn't want me. I was dependent on him for a word of affection and encouragement; he was dependent on my young shoulder to guide him.

Billy's sole pleasure was an old clay pipe. Each evening we'd sit together on Mrs Burke's back stairs, the blue smoke swirling in a hazy cloud about us, and he'd talk of the days of long ago when his sight was the sight of a hovering hawk and his strong body straight as the mast of his ship, dancing to the rhythm of the surging seas.

"Ah sure, 'tis a grand life, the sea, Jamsie lad – the lick of the salt on your face, the buck of the deck to your feet. That's the only life, shipmate, and don't you believe the word of a man who'd say 'tis not."

And I'd close my eyes and Billy's hypnotic tongue would make tropical trees tremble to a dancing breeze, or taut sheets would scream and the decks would heave and we beating it round the Horn or facing into a typhoon in the South China Seas. And his voice would grow husky when he talked of his mates, and when I'd ask "Where's Captain Johnson now, Billy?" or "Do you ever meet up with Boson Brown now, Billy?", there would come a tremble in his throat and a sad loneliness in his wrinkled face.

"When the owld eyes gave out on me, Jamsie lad, I had to put the past behind me. 'Tis very lonely being blind – very, very lonely indeed. Nobody needs me now and the salt sea, well, it don't need me nather."

Then he'd sigh and cheer up and say: "Ah, shure, 'tis God's will. And, anyway, haven't I the great owld shipmate in you." And that would make me proud, very, very proud. Then he'd tap out the pipe on Mrs Burke's stairs and I'd know it was time to take him to the church to say his rosary.

It was on Christmas Eve that he broke the pipe. It was never a beautiful thing, with its cracked stem spliced with fine twine and its bowl chipped and brown and charred.

Billy and I had sailed afar that night. Outside, the driving wind was lashing the snow into a frenzy but Billy had whisked me abroad to a tropical clime where Christmas came in the middle of summer.

"'Tis quare out, Jamsie lad. You'd be there bidding health and prosperity to folk on Christmas Day and the big sun riding high in the hot sky, and the sultry air like a blanket on the face of the sea. And you'd be thinking of the people back home and they shivering cowld on a night such as this, and they humped to the heat of an owld sod. Sure, 'tis almost pagan when you think of it, Jamsie. But they do quare things abroad...'tis the sun, I'd say."

And he tapped out the pipe. Maybe his mind was still on faraway place, for he normally exercised the greatest of care at this solemn operation of cleaning out the pipe. But there it was, the stem in his hand, the bowl in bits on the floor.

"Is it – is it broken?" His words were a whimper of real fear.

"Ah, it'll be easy to fix," I said but he knew and I knew that the hope was a lie. His old hands trembled.

"'Twas a good pipe even though 'twas old, and we've travelled a fair bit together. And 'twas all that was left to me of the past . . . "

That's what hurt most, I think. The long, full years stretched back in his mind and that pipe was the link that bound the memory of the past with the reality of the present. And the link had snapped. The ghost of a smile came hovering to his lips.

"Like the Christmases abroad, 'twill be a quare Christmas without the pipe." But he put it from him with fortitude. "Let's be off to the Church, Jamsie. There's nothing wrong that a few prayers won't put right."

I loved Blind Billy. He was the only person in the whole world that I loved. Here it was Christmas, I thought to myself, and Christmas wasn't supposed to be a time for sorrow. But even my childish mind could grasp that Christmas without the pipe would be a torture for Billy.

As we fought our way through the snow, my mind was at work. I knew Jordan's shop – the pipes, row upon row of them, shiny and black, straight pipes and curled pipes. How often I had touched them – the sleek roundness of their fat bowls, the flowing lines of their long stems – and smiled at the thought of Billy's old clay. But Billy couldn't afford one of them. It was Christmas and that didn't seem right . . .

The Church was almost empty. As he knelt beside Father Blake's box, Billy's beads danced to the rhythm of his prayers. He never heard me going, and long before the last decade had rolled through his fingers, I was back in my place beside him, the stolen pipe a warm bump in my gansey.

I meant to wait till we were back in the frugal comfort of his lodgings before offering him my present, but Billy sensed my pent-up excitement.

"You left the Church, Jamsie lad. What mischief were you up to now?"

My heart jumped at that. "No mischief at all, Billy." I pulled the pipe from under my gansey and put it into his cold hand. "I bought you a pipe for Christmas. I've been saving up for a present for you for months . . . "

Billy stopped in his surprise. He fingered the pipe gently, caressing its shiny slimness. For a moment he couldn't speak.

"A pipe, Jamsie? For me? A present?" There was a queer quiver in his voice that made my heart fill with a pleasure I had never before experienced. "A new pipe for me! Why, Jamsie, Jamsie lad, I don't know what to say. 'Tis so long since anything was given to me from the goodness of the heart that I'd well-nigh forgotten . . . " His hand squeezed my shoulder so hard I could cry, but the pain was the delicious pain of love and I laughed and laughed and danced in my excitement.

"Do you like it Billy? Do you really like it? Here, try it!" And I snapped it from him and pushed the stem into his mouth. His teeth clamped on it and he sucked and he blew and he blew and he sucked.

"'Tis surely the grandest pipe in the whole world!" And he laughed and I laughed with him, and there we stood in the cold and the snow and the wind howling about us, and we clapped each other on the back, and we laughed some more.

"Thank you, thank you, Jamsie lad!" He kept repeating it, his head swaying proudly from side to side, and the pipe, a symbol of my love, in his mouth. "This is the nicest thing that has ever happened to me. I'll remember this to my dying day . . . "

And the cold wind shifted to hush the words as if knowing how close that day was.

From the corner of our street I saw the policeman, big and menacing, walking towards my aunt's door. Panic leapt like a fire inside me. Fright made a fool of my tongue.

"Quick, Billy, hide! For God's sake, hide!" I was pulling him by the tail of his coat. "There's a policeman at my aunt's door . . . "

I wish I had died just then. I wish I had never been born to see my old friend's face collapse in a mixture of utter disappointment and anger and sorrow, all merged into one.

"You stole the pipe, Jamsie." It wasn't a question – he knew. I was crying then.

"But I only did it for you, Billy. You needed a pipe and sure owld Jordan has millions of 'em." An awful thought struck me. "You won't give me away, will you Billy?" You won't tell the police? Don't tell them I left the church. Say I stayed with you all the time."

Billy almost pushed me from him. He handed me the pipe. "God forgive you, Jamsie lad" he whispered. And I knew that his whole world had collapsed about him there in the snow.

"You won't tell, Billy, will you?" His head shook slowly, painfully.

"No Jamsie lad, I won't tell." And he turned and he tap-tap-tapped his way through the dark of the night, his tired old body bent, his shoulders hunched into the freezing wind. Our street seemed darker than I had ever seen it before, and I cried. Oh God, how I cried!

He never told. He was dead when they found him, a

small pathetic bundle, alone and frozen, his beads in his hand. Cold and exposure, the coroner said. But I knew.

For 60 years I've known and for 60 years I've tried to forget. One hundred, a thousand times I've searched that pipe from my sea-bag to hurl it into the depths of the oceans I've sailed. But always I paused. No, no, no that's not the way – that's not the place for Billy's present.

And now, at last, it's all over. Today, on Christmas Eve, I found poor Billy's grave – a pauper's grave, unmarked, untended. There on my knees in the swirling snow I prayed: "Billy! Blind Billy, hear me now and forgive me. I've paid for your pipe. I went into Jordan's shop today, 60 long years too late, and I paid what I owed."

Then I scooped a hole in the sodden clay and I buried the pipe above him. "Take it, Billy," I pleaded. "Please Billy. It's really yours now – a Christmas gift from me to you . . . "

And then I heard it – the voice from the past sounded clear in my ears. I'll swear it as long as I live.

"Thanks, Jamsie. Thanks, Jamsie lad. 'Tis a grand pipe and a lovely present indeed. I'm glad to accept it..."

And there in the snow I wept with the warmth of forgiveness.

CROSSING THE LINE

RTÉ, *Sunday Miscellany*, April 1993

Sailors the world over acknowledge that King Neptune, God of the Ocean and the Deep, is the most powerful and cantankerous of all the ancient Gods. With a curt nod of his noble head he raises storms that lash the oceans to a mighty frenzy, sinking and destroying all before them. With a benevolent wave of his shell-encrusted arm he spreads a benign smile across the face of those same oceans and changes their furrowed wrinkled features from frustrated anger to mirrored calm.

For thousands of years, generations of exploring mariners recognised the might of Neptune and meekly hove-to in mid-ocean before daring to sail their ships across the long line of the equator. In the ancient Ceremony of Crossing the Line, Captains of ships, be they tourist liners, powerful men-of-war, rusty old tankers or clippers under full sail, they all submitted to the authority of King Neptune and humbly begged His Majesty's permission to proceed. It was a Festive Day and King Neptune reigned supreme.

I first crossed the line, 15 December 1941. It was wartime and our ship was diverted urgently from convoy duties in the North Atlantic to help counter the advance of Japanese forces in the Indian Ocean. The U-boat-infested Atlantic was no place to hove-to, but our Captain, an old sea-dog who respected the might and majesty of King Neptune, compromised by swinging the ship hard to port to sail a course along the line of the equator while seeking permission to proceed across. And so the formal ceremony of Crossing the Line began.

The senior Boson's Mate played King Neptune, naked under a long cloak; his greasy hair was plaited from seaweed. He and his entourage, a group of painted, near-naked seamen, emerged from the shelter of a lifeboat and took command of the flight deck. A throne had been erected in front of a large canvas swimming pool and there for the rest of the afternoon watch, King Neptune, a wicked-looking trident in his right hand, held court.

The Captain was the first to pay homage. Bowing low before His Majesty, he humbly requested permission to sail his ship into the Southern Hemisphere. Questioned extensively and haughtily about his navigational qualifications for such a task, and whether he had, in fact, ever previously taken a ship across the line, Neptune finally agreed to allow the ship to proceed. In return, however, he demanded that each sailor on board who had not previously crossed the line should be brought before him to ascertain his worthiness to enter the Kingdom of the Deep.

King Neptune's forte is humiliation. Sailor after sailor was arrested by marauding aides, and dragged, kicking and protesting into the Royal Presence. Humiliating questions about our lineage and legitimacy had to be answered and ribald physical examination of our manhood or otherwise was silently endured. Then, our naked bodies were roughly scrubbed with long-handled deck brushes, soft soap blinding and choking us, and our heads were crudely shaved with large plywood razors. In a final act of humiliation, we were, one by one, dumped bodily into the canvas swimming-pool there to be ducked repeatedly till we managed to escape, half-drowned, to the safety of the mess.

Then, the ancient ceremony of Crossing the Line fully enacted, King Neptune returned to the Deep, his historic lordship over the oceans of the world firmly re-established. Even in war, King Neptune could not be ignored.

Today, new-fangled ships of the sky daily carry thousands of travellers across the equator without permission or by your leave. Vessels of trade, bound only by economic constraints, plough their paths through the oceans of the world, the equator just another line on their charts.

And a furious King Neptune sulks in the deep, his authority flouted, his mighty presence ignored.

However, all the signs and omens point to the inevitable fact that King Neptune, his royal patience exhausted, is fighting back. Recent years have set an unfortunate record level for wholesale destruction and death caused by hurricanes, typhoons and tidal waves. El Nino and Hurricane Mitch wrought havoc in Central America. Earthquakes on the ocean bed caused catastrophes the likes of which had never before been experienced and resultant huge tidal waves swept all before them. Turkey, Greece, China, South Africa, they have all felt the wrath of Neptune.

And so, as we move further into the New Millennium, scientists continue to blame global warning for all climatic changes. But the people of the world might fare better if they heed the heavenly signs and portents for what they are and pay homage at the equator, as did our forefathers, to His Gracious Majesty, King Neptune, Lord of the Oceans and the Deep. He is reclaiming his ancient Kingdom. His hour is now. We continue to ignore him at our peril.

Moscow's Red Letter Day

Irish Press, September 1977

The unsmiling policeman on duty at one of the entrance roads to Moscow's Red Square put his hand on my chest and pushed. There was no doubting the unspoken message – nobody was allowed into Red Square today. That evening on Moscow TV I saw the reason for the closure – heads of Communist states, on a visit to Moscow to celebrate the sixth anniversary of the October 1st Revolution, were laying wreaths at the Lenin Mausoleum. Neither tourists like myself nor ordinary Russian citizens were allowed to watch. One wondered who in fact, was celebrating the 60th anniversary of the Workers' Revolution.

Moscow is a city of startling architectural contrasts: tall, modern, glass and concrete offices, and towering apartment blocks dwarf centuries-old cathedrals whose gold-plated domes and cupolas glitter and glisten in the blinding November sunlight.

Any visitor to the Soviet capital goes first of all to Red Square and the Kremlin. This is the throbbing, if cold, heart of Moscow. Tent-roofed towers rise above its battlements, and beyond them can be seen the golden domes of white stone cathedrals and the silvery roofs of palaces.

The Cathedral of St Basil, dominating Red Square, was built in honour of the final liberation of the Russian

State from Tartar dependency. Ivan the Terrible commissioned the cathedral in 1552 and it looks like it will stand forever, a legend in colourful stone, and a monument to the inimitable beauty of early Russian architecture. Tradition says that Ivan had the architect's eyes gouged out when the building was completed so that he would never match again the beauty of his creation.

The official signs of preparations for the celebrations were everywhere. Coloured lights, by the mile, hung like necklaces on the bridges and main roads converging on Red Square and the Kremlin. Huge pictures of the stern, handsome face of Lenin, the father of the revolution, were draped on every building. Red flags fluttered in profusion in every breeze. Large signs proclaimed that: "To work is the joy of the People", and "Glory to the workers!"

And the workers of Moscow plodded along the wide car-free boulevards. Nowhere else will you see many people walking. Nowhere else will you see so many unsmiling faces.

Let me dispel at once any notions of Hollywood-type evil men, in felt hats and long overcoats, tailing foreign tourists around the city. We were allowed to roam freely. We travelled on crowded buses, trolley cars, taxis and the underground railway system. We walked through shops and cafes without any let or official hindrance. Of course, on the day we arrived in Moscow, our passports, visas and return airline tickets had been taken from us at the hotel 'for registration'.

The Moscow underground railway system, the Metro, is surely the most amazing in the world. The fact that it efficiently transports two billion people a year in fast, clean and punctual trains fades to insignificance in the face of the beauty of the underground complex, shining with polished oak and walnut, ceramics and plate glass, granite and marble and crystal.

For five kopeks (4p) one can travel its whole 150-kilometre length. But do stop at each underground station, get out of the train and admire in astonishment the shining chandeliers, the bronze statues and the priceless paintings. Here is a free, public cultural attraction that cannot be surpassed. And, as a final boast, the proud Muscovite will tell you that the excellent ventilation system provides fresh air and an even temperature the whole year round.

The magnificence of the Metro could never be equalled by the Hotel Ukraine where we stayed, but the hotel does attempt to match its splendour. It was built in 1953 and has over 1,000 rooms but its grandeur is part of a past age. My single room measured 18' x 18' with a 12' high ceiling. Two full French doors opened onto a balcony with a sweeping panoramic view of Moscow and the river. The furniture was made of inlaid walnut; the curtains of heavy velvet and each room had a television and radio. The attached carpeted bathroom was fully equipped, including a massive bath, and unusual in Moscow, the water was always hot.

Despite its architectural attractions, Moscow does not seem to be the place to visit if you want to meet the Russian people. A picture in a Russian guidebook shows an evening city scene, with the caption; "In the evenings the neon signs of cafes and restaurants light up – here Muscovites meet friends, celebrate birthdays, wedding anniversaries, the first nights of a new play..."

Whilst there are numerous cinemas, theatres, the Moscow State Circus and, of course, the famous Balshoi Ballet, bars or pubs as we know them in Ireland, don't exist, and any attempt to strike up a conversation with a stranger is politely, or rudely, shrugged off. You will, of course, be exposed to propaganda about the glories of the revolution – after all, they are celebrating its 60th anniversary! On a wet Sunday afternoon a guided tour took us to the Museum of the Workers' Revolution. A portly female guide talked at length before each exhibit portraying the life and career of the Hero Lenin, and the interpreter droned it to us in English. Phrases like "the assurance of victory in the historic battle for communist ideals", and "the purity of the ideals of our glorious Lenin" reeled off the Russian tongues with patriotic zeal. A three-dimensional reconstruction of the charge of the Tsar's Cossacks on the red-flagged barricades, manned by glorious workers was backed by martial music and an emotional harangue, which fortunately, was not translated for us. There was, however, proud fervour on the faces of the guide and the interpreter. And it was while this hymn of glory was ringing out that a young Irish student in our group was approached by two Russian youths who bought his jeans for £80, a quick transfer being done in the toilet.

If Lenin's Mausoleum wasn't under constant surveillance in Red Square, the unfortunate man would surely have turned in his grave.

THE DARK SHADOW OF THE IRISH WORKHOUSE

Ireland's Own, May 2001

"The poor you have always with ye," Jesus told his disciples. And he could have added "and the beggars and the vagabonds, the aged, the infirm and the widows and the orphans." In fact, it was to control the social problems caused by such unfortunate people that the concept of the workhouse was first conceived in England.

Since medieval times English society has been structured on a class system based on wealth and breeding. There was always an upper class, a middle class and a working class, but languishing at the very bottom of this social scale were the paupers and the vagabonds. And in the bureaucratic mind, this group was a shiftless section of society so bone idle that they'd rather beg from their betters than do an honest day's work. It was for them that the workhouse system was introduced.

Altruism was never a factor in the official approach. Workhouses were not built for the alleviation of hunger or the well-being of the sick – they were to be detention and correction centres for beggars and vagabonds where, hopefully, under harsh conditions and strict supervision, these chronic idlers would learn to embrace the work ethic and become responsible members of society. And to this end the guiding principle of the workhouse rule was that: "inmates must be worse fed, worse clothed and worse lodged than the independent labourers of the district and no individual capable of exertion must ever be permitted to be idle."

In Ireland paupers had always been more fortunate. Under the Brehon Laws, their place in society was established in the ancient clan system. That place may have been a lowly one but it carried its rights and it catered for the basic needs of the poor. Then came the Christian era with its monastic system, and Ireland became famed as the Island of saints and scholars. This period peaked with the arrival of wealthy Norman barons who built and maintained many of our famous monasteries, and because the kindly abbots of the Franciscans, the Augustinians and Cistercians were bound by their Holy Orders never to turn the poor from their doors, the poor survived. In 1466, however, everything changed.

When Henry VIII proclaimed the Protestant Reformation, all Irish monastery lands were confiscated and planted by English settlers. With the ancient Irish clan system long since broken down and the monasteries now closed, what had previously been poverty in Ireland quickly degenerated into abject destitution. And to solve the problem the English workhouse system was introduced – from now on the Irish poor must be forced to work before any relief would be provided. In 1838 a massive construction programme to build 130 workhouses was put in place. The timing was fortuitous.

During the next decade the potato crop failed again and again and famine spread across the land. Very quickly a new breed of poor was spawned. The once proud small-holders of Ireland, now unable to pay the usurious rent to absentee landlords, were evicted from their land. They, with their wives and children, were forced by hunger and disease to flock to workhouses already overcrowded with wandering beggars and vagabonds. Wrote a historian of the time: "Bantry workhouse, which was designed to cater for 600 inmates, now holds 2,237 persons and 600 children. Here even their misery does not terminate – the resources of the Union are exhausted and the establishment is in debt to a fearful amount..." In effect, within a short span of ten years, the much vaunted workhouse system had collapsed.

Today, 160 years on, while some of the workhouses have fallen into decay, many have been refurbished and are now modern hospitals and day-care centres caring for the sick and the poor. Despite their new role, however, the memory of the shame and humiliation that the workhouse system once brought upon our people will always cast a long, dark shadow across the pages of Irish history.

THE PRIEST OF THE LUBYANKA

Evening Herald, September 1982

Daily Mass in Moscow was my personal act of defiance that brightened a week's stay in the heart of communist Russia. I wasn't always sure who or what I was defying, or whether such an act was truly Christian. But it made me feel good.

Finding the 150-vear-old Church of St Ludovig was surprisingly easy –the receptionist at the Hotel Ukraine gave me full details of its location and Mass times, and obligingly wrote the address of the church on the cover of my chequebook.

The taxidriver took one glance at her cryptic instructions and we were on our way. However, ten minutes later, when he dropped me and pointed across to the small building partly hidden by a dilapidated corrugated iron fence, my troubles started.

We had arrived in Moscow at ten o'clock the previous night and there had been no opportunity to change our money into Russian roubles. Seasonal travellers had assured me that taxidrivers, particularly, would be delighted to accept payment in sterling – and the exchange rates would be right! My man seemed to be the inevitable exception.

His eyes popped in horror when I thrust a crisp new five-pound note into his hand. "Nyet, nyet!" he recoiled and broke into a torrent of anxious Russian. I tried to explain in my best pidgin English that I had no roubles and, anyhow, wasn't a fiver in sterling far better than the three roubles he was demanding? He waved the money away in indignation.

The two Russian policemen, standing at the imposing doors of the building beside us watched in steely silence. It was nearly eight o'clock and I didn't want to be late for my first Mass in Russia. I stuffed the note into his jacket pocket. He snatched it out as if it had burnt him, threw it on the ground at my feet, and was gone in a squeal of protesting tyres. The policemen just watched with that chilling attitude of apparent disinterest that Russian policemen can so readily project.

Three hours later I discovered that I had been conducting my highly illegal currency transactions outside the gates of the dreaded Lubyanka prison. Eight stories high, all windows grimly shuttered, with further stories below street level, this notorious place is the headquarters of the KGB where the victims of communist terrorism are held and tortured. Many who have entered its dreaded gates have never again seen the light of day. No wonder my unfortunate taxidriver was shocked and frightened. St Ludovig, in his little church beneath the shadows of this grim fortress, had been looking after me that morning, just as he had looked after the Catholic population of Moscow for over 150 years.

St Ludovig's is the only Catholic church in Moscow. It is a small, dark but beautiful, Romanesque in style, seating about 200 people. Like the many Russian Orthodox churches in the city, it is almost vulgarly ornate with brass candelabra, electric candles, icons, side altars, statues and gaudy pictures. But it has a quiet peaceful atmosphere that inspires prayer – the feeling perhaps of being in a beleaguered oasis in the middle of a vast communist desert. It creates a strange feeling of vibrant Christianity – there was a similar feeling in the Phoenix Park on the morning of the Pope's visit in 1979.

Father Stanislaus, a Lithuanian, has been the Parish Priest since 1967 and he is the only Catholic priest in Moscow. His daily Mass at eight o'clock was attended by, on average, 18 elderly Russian women and myself. The women were grey-haired, small and plump with woollen headscarves, thick stockings and heavy boots. Up to then my only experience of life in Russia had been gleaned from American films and these women could have walked into the church straight from a Hollywood set.

Their humble piety was, however, inspiring. Many of them ignored the dubious comfort of the wooden kneeling stools and seats and knelt on the cold flagged floor in the aisles. At the moment of consecration their foreheads touched down to the stone in adoration. The wooden plate that the deacon passed around reflected the abject poverty of the small congregation – the pathetic jingle of kopek coins could hardly have added up to a total collection of twenty pence. Yet there seemed to be no shortage of money in Moscow. On three different occasions during my week's stay I had been offered sums ranging from £60 to £90 in roubles for a watch I bought in Youghal six years before for a mere £5 – the last occasion was in, of all places, the Museum of the Workers' Republic. The black market was a thriving if highly dangerous way of life in Moscow.

My last morning in the little church of St Ludovig appeared to coincide with a day of special devotion for the Moscow church. The building was ablaze with electric candles, and the smell of incense hung heavy in the air. Father Stanislaus sang his Mass in Latin to the

accompaniment of a male-voice choir, backed by
magnificent organ music – all on tape! The acoustics
were far from perfect but the timing was novel and
extremely clever. "Dominus vobis cum," chanted Father
Stanislaus. "Et cum spiritu tuo," boomed back the taped
choir. The deacon, in between serving the Mass, delicately
controlled the volume and pace of the responses from the
recorder and at the appropriate times the small church
throbbed to the stirring verses of the taped hymns.

And the old women bowed their heads till they touched
the cold stone slabs. God was very much present in that
small corner of Russia. Now without a watch, I was not
sure how long it took to sing the Mass that morning but
when the wooden plate came around I slipped nearly
£100 worth of roubles in with the silvery kopeks. And if
the end justifies the means, then St Ludovig was smiling
happily, and Father Stanislaus, when he counted up his
collection, surely must have felt that Christmas had arrived
a little early that year.

And when we came out into the cold sunshine of the
Moscow morning, the dark shadows of the grim Lubyanka
prison didn't seem so menacing or frightening any more.

A WARNING TO WORMS

Irish Monthly, June 1949

I admit without argument that the worm will turn. But is he better off after turning? Will the early bird that missed him before swoop down and gobble him up when this new, juicy side is exposed to the gaze. There's the rub. Take the case of Mr Hackett.

Mr Albert Hackett was, to put it crudely, a worm of the less offensive kind. He wanted, more than anything else in the world, to be left strictly alone. I'm sure you know his type. They are small. They have long, lean necks sticking out of stiff white collars. And they wear bowler hats. He was quite happy, though, was Mr Albert Hackett. He worked hard and conscientiously in the offices of the local brewery. He had never been promoted, nor, indeed, considered for promotion. He lived alone in a rented room and he was civil to everybody to the point of servility. I'm sure Albert, himself, would not object to my comparing him with a worm. However, it doesn't matter now whether he would or not. He turned and he was gobbled up.

Though Mr Hackett shunned all company as a rule, he was a member of the local workingman's club. From his days in the Local Defence Force he had retained a love for the game of billiards; that was the only reason he was a member. On the night of his turning we find him waiting for his crony, Mr Joseph Beckett, on the corner of the street. The only reason you must meet Joe is that he always managed to beat our hero at billiards. Every night for ten years or so they went up to the club together. Every night they played a hundred up. And every night Joe beat Albert – not decisively, mark you. No! He always got one or two of a lead and managed to retain it to the end.

That's about the only thing that ever stirred the beast in Mr Hackett. The only ambition he cherished was to trounce Mr Beckett once and for all, and he swore to himself that if he could do that, he'd give up the game for good. Ten years is a long time. Three thousand six hundred and fifty odd games and just 'pipped' in every one of them. It undermines a chap's morale. So ran his thoughts as he watched Joe approach.

"Evening, Albert. All ready for your beating?" Thus the tactless Mr Beckett.

"Evening, Joe," grunted Albert and maintained a dignified silence as they made their way towards the club. They understood each other. They were worms of a feather, if you'll excuse the mixed metaphor.

"Seems to be something going on by the looks of things," said Mr Beckett as they approached the corrugated-iron building.

"Yes, indeed. There does seem to be something going on," agreed Mr Hackett mildly. Lights blazed from every window. "Damnation," he added in an unusual flash of inspiration. "It's the whist drive, the annual whist drive! Which means women all over the place as usual. Something should be done about it. It's a man's club. No place for women to be . . . !"

That was another aspect of Mr Hackett's character you should know about. He would never admit it to you or me, but he was very frightened of women. He avoided them like the plague.

"Ah well," said Mr Beckett philosophically, "we'll have

our game and clear out of the place. We can have a few jars down at Tim Joe's . . . "

They entered the building and turned into the main bar. The tables had been placed in two long lines down the centre and the crudely-painted number cards tacked on them gave mute confirmation of Mr Hackett's surmise about a whist-drive. If further evidence were needed that women were expected in this sanctum of the working male, there was the vase of flowers on the bar. Mr Hackett peered at the flowers with distaste.

"Oh good! Hackett! Beckett! Just in time! Put these scorecards on the tables, will you. You take the ladies, Hackett, and you take the gents, Beckett." Mr O'Rourke, the club secretary-cum-barman, was another thing Mr Hackett thought something should be done about. He was the hail-fellow-well-met, overpowering type. He was the early bird who catches worms, we might say, as we are working that particular metaphor. Our hero and his crony were his particular worms. He bullied them and they did what they were told without demur.

"I'm worked to death, as usual," he groaned, thrusting a bundle of scorecards into their unwilling hands. "Always rushing about looking after your interests and organising your entertainment." He flopped into a nearby armchair and raised his pint to his lips. "And don't you fellows expect me to be serving drinks to you in there in the billiard-room tonight. I'll be much too busy looking after our lady guests . . . " He gulped his pint noisily as he watched them distribute the cards. Then he went behind the bar to fill himself another pint.

Mr Hackett often wondered if the secretary ever paid for the numerous pints he consumed but, of course, he never mentioned things like that out loud. No, indeed, not even to Mr Beckett. They finished their unwelcome chore and slipped into the curtained-off portion of the bar, known as the billiard-room.

"Infernal nuisance, that fellow," whispered Joe to Albert as he selected his cue.

"Aar," said Albert, hanging his jacket carefully on a nail beside the scoreboard. "Your turn to break off tonight, Joe."

"Right! Spot 'em up and I'll give you another lesson in the art of billiard playing." Joe was like that – always rubbing it in but in a nice sort of way, of course.

The game started just like the other three thousand, six hundred and fifty odd games before it. Joe took the lead and looked like holding it to the end. But he didn't hold it. That's why this tale is being told. It is for you to decide whether it would have been better for Mr Hackett if, on this fateful night, he had been just 'pipped' as usual. It is for you – but let me explain how things turned out.

The score stood at 76–74 in Joe Beckett's favour. They were both on top of their form, intent and anxious for victory. The noisy chatter of arriving couples was ignored, relegated to rightful obscurity by this struggle between giants. Then Joe missed a simple pot.

"Aar!" said Mr Hackett. His breath came through his teeth in a long, low whistle. He gripped his cue tightly to control the tremor that ran through his body. Joe stared at the table aghast at his mistake.

"A sell-out," he groaned. Hope surged through Mr Hackett as he weighed up the situation. The red ball was in position just by the top left-hand pocket. Joe's ball was four inches from the right middle pocket, and Mr Hackett was in the semi-circle an inch from the baulk-line.

It was, indeed, a sell-out. Twenty-six to get and Albert told himself fiercely that if he couldn't get 26 from that position he was a Dutchman. I hasten to add that our hero was a proud Irishman who, though he was too young to have been in the GPO during Easter Week, he did have a Certificate for his service with the Local Defence Force during the Emergency. He worked it all out carefully: in off the white and leave Joe's ball by the top pocket, in off the red and . . . but it was all there, the handiest 26 of his life. There would be a beating: 100 – 74! A rout! Beckett would never dare brag again. His ambition realised at last! He drew a long breath and took careful aim. Then it happened.

"Hackett! Beckett! Okay, break it up. I need you." The club secretary came bounding through the curtains like a lion leaping on its prey.

"Mrs O'Neill has brought along her widowed sister and her daughter and that leaves me two men short so you two will have to join in. Come along now, the ladies are waiting . . . " He reached out to sweep the balls into the pockets. Mr Hackett saw the two thin hands hovering over the table like the grasping talons of a hovering hawk. He saw his chance of victory slipping away forever. Ten years of patient effort wasted. Mr Beckett was putting away his cue with an air of resignation. Something seemed to snap inside Mr Hackett.

"Don't you dare touch those balls, O'Rourke!" His voice cracked like a whip across the table. Mr Beckett stopped with his cue half-way in the rack and stood like a soldier with his rifle in the 'at ease' position. Mr O'Rourke jerked back his hands and stared with popping eyes at the balls on the green cloth. If they had suddenly turned into balls of molten steel his amazement would not have been greater. Mr Hackett stood straight as his sergeant major used to stand on parade. His lean face was pale with his towering anger.

"You heard what I said, O'Rourke," he barked. "Leave those balls where they are." He breathed noisily through his nose. "And get out of here. And stay out until you're called. When men are playing billiards, silence will be observed in the billiard room. That's a club rule." Mr Hackett was warming to it. "There are a few more rules too with which you are not apparently familiar. If you wish to retain your job here I suggest that you should brush up on them. I'll be speaking to the Chairman later about your general conduct . . . "

Mr O'Rourke stood petrified. The tip of Mr Hackett's cue waved under the secretary's nose. He retreated through the curtains. The chatter in the main bar stopped. Only the stern ringing tones of the new Mr Hackett broke the morgue-like silence.

"Mr Beckett and I came here to play billiards, not whist, and we will not be disturbed. Now, get out!" He punctuated his last remark with fierce jabs of the cue in Mr O'Rourke's chest.

"I'm sure I'm sorry, Mr Hackett," stuttered the amazed club secretary. "No offence meant, I'm sure, sir!" And he quickly escaped the kingly anger by retreating through the curtains. The worm had turned. Mr Hackett had come of age. He was, at last, a man.

"Begorr!" whispered the amazed Mr Beckett, "you certainly put him in his place, Albert, I'll say!" His eyes were full of worshipping admiration. Mr Hackett sagged slightly as the breath whistled out of him.

"About time too! I've been meaning to do that for some time," he said. He drew himself up to his full five foot six. "Now let's get on with the game." He tried to conceal his elation, but his new-found manhood surged up and down inside him like a flooded river trying to burst its banks. In off the white, then in off the red... a rout – a decisive rout! First Mr O'Rourke and then Mr Beckett. Tonight would go down as a red-letter night in the long history of the club. His fingers trembled slightly.

"I think a drink is indicated, Joe!" he said. He walked to the curtains and put his head through. An awed silence fell on the excited crowd at the tables. All eyes were upon him. His face reddened ever so slightly.

"O'Rourke," he called in authoritative tones. "O'Rourke! Bring two pints in here. Right away."

"Yes, Mr Hackett," said O'Rourke. "Right away, sir." The victory was complete. The worm had shown his nice new juicy side to the public. And the public overwhelmingly approved.

But, already, an early bird was on the wing. As Mr Hackett turned, his eyes met those of Mrs O'Neill's widowed sister. She smiled warmly. Mr Hackett hesitated, surprised. She winked invitingly. Mr Hackett had never experienced anything like this before. Suddenly his new-found manhood seemed to surge higher and higher as if aspiring to greater deeds, more manly affairs. Mrs O'Neill's widowed sister's pink tongue touched temptingly around her full red lips. Mr Hackett went all soft inside. He looked back at the balls on the table. In off the white and then in off the red . . . an easy 26: too easy, in fact, for the new Mr Hackett. He looked back again at Mrs O'Neill's widowed sister. It was then that his few-found manhood engulfed him. In fact, it betrayed him.

"Mr Beckett," he said, "I've got your measure at last. I can beat you at billiards." He grasped his crony's arm and led him from the billiard room. "Tonight, however, we'll play whist . . . " and he sat down opposite Mrs O'Neill's widowed sister.

Which all goes to illustrate my point because he'd be a far happier worm today if he'd never turned. They had been married only a month when she stopped him going to the club altogether. So if there's a worm amongst my readers – brother, you've been warned!

Questions in Prague

RTÉ, *Sunday Miscellany*, June 1987

Travelling in Eastern Europe is no longer the exciting adventure it used to be. There's no dark mystery any more, no lurking suspicions, no hostile scrutiny of documents. It's not like the bad old days when every Western traveller was a suspected spy.

I once had a revolver held to my head by a female border guard at the checkpoint between Vienna and Brno. What aroused her suspicions was the fact that my travel documents stated that I would enter Czechoslovakia directly from London to Prague. Why then was I coming in from Vienna? It took two hours of questioning and some telephone calls to her superiors before she reluctantly accepted that British Airways, due to overbooking, had rearranged my travel schedule. The fact that the guard was about twenty-three years old with ash blonde hair and was very beautiful didn't make the experience any the less frightening.

Fortunately, travelling behind the Iron Curtain, which I did regularly as a journalist, wasn't always full of fear and uncertainty – it sometimes had its moments of black comedy.

Once I remember I had flown into Prague from Brno and a guide who introduced himself as Emile met me at the airport. He was, he told me, eighty-two years old and his full-time job was escorting visiting foreigners to their hotels. When we were settled into the waiting taxi he produced a clipboard and biro.

"If you don't mind," he said, "there are some questions I must ask." I told him to fire away. His first question was to establish that he had my name spelled correctly. When I confirmed that it was so, he ticked off the question with a flourish.

"You come from Dublin, Ireland?" I nodded and he ticked again.

"You wish to stay in Prague for three days?" I nodded; he ticked.

"You wish to stay at the Hotel Intercontinental?" Another nod, and another tick. Then: "Do you wish for a horizontal companion?" I thought about that for a puzzled moment or two before the penny dropped.

"Emile!" I said in disbelief, "are you asking me if I want a woman?" He shrugged his shoulders.

"Or a man or a boy whichever is your preference." His biro was poised waiting over the clipboard.

"Lookit here," I said indignantly, "I'll have you know that I'm a happily married man. I've been married for 35 years and –" He cut me off with a wave of the biro.

"Please, please, not to be annoyed," he said, his voice patient. "You understand I have to ask these questions, and that was merely question number five."

That was 14 years ago. The Iron Curtain is gone; the Berlin Wall has been demolished and with them went the dark brooding mystery, the fear and the uncertainty that could change a business trip into a frightening adventure.

Unfortunately, with them too went those fragile touches of black comedy that often helped light up what was then a very dark scene.

Going Home

Cork Weekly Examiner
September 1951

The candle that is Life flickered and I saw
Death stand before me.
He smiled at me in welcome; I cried and
backed away in fear.
But now the candle flickers low and
the darkness closes more about me
no longer do I dread the Spectre figure
who stands with arms outstretched
for I see a Light behind him and my
heart is touched with some content.
I was promised much.
I have deep trust.
I wait.
I pray